cichlids of the world

by Dr. Robert J. Goldstein

Distributed in the UNITED STATES by T.F.H. Publications, Inc., One T.F.H. Plaza, Neptune City, NJ 07753; in CANADA to the Pet Trade by H & L Pet Supplies Inc., 27 Kingston Crescent, Kitchener, Ontario N2B 2T6; Rolf C. Hagen Ltd., 3225 Sartelon Street, Montreal 382 Quebec; in CANADA to the Book Trade by Macmillan of Canada (A Division of Canada Publishing Corporation), 164 Commander Boulevard, Agincourt, Ontario M1S 3C7; in ENGLAND by T.F.H. Publications Limited, Cliveden House/Priors Way/Bray, Maidenhead, Berkshire SL6 2HP, England; in AUSTRALIA AND THE SOUTH PACIFIC by T.F.H. (Australia) Pty. Ltd., Box 149, Brookvale 2100 N.S.W., Australia; in NEW ZEALAND by Ross Haines & Son, Ltd., 18 Monmouth Street, Grey Lynn, Auckland 2, New Zealand; in SINGAPORE AND MALAYSIA by MPH Distributors (S) Pte., Ltd., 601 Sims Drive, #03/07/21, Singapore 1438; in the PHILIPPINES by Bio-Research, 5 Lippay Street, San Lorenzo Village, Makati Rizal; in SOUTH AFRICA by Multipet Pty. Ltd., 30 Turners Avenue, Durban 4001. Published by T.F.H. Publications, Inc. Manufactured in the United States of America by T.F.H. Publications, Inc.

Preface

In 1969 I completed a major effort which was subsequently published as CICHLIDS by TFH in 1970. Comments ranged from "*not bad for him*" to "*looks like a one week effort,*" and suddenly my mailbox was filled with corrections, references to pertinent literature, copies of literature, hand-written letters of experiences, observations, and hearsay. In no time at all my stack of observations and data grew to mammoth proportions. The reason, apparently, was that this was the first serious attempt to bring aquarium knowledge of cichlids up to date and in line with the scattered bits of knowledge shared or distributed among aquarists, ichthyologists, fisheries biologists, and behaviorists. Thus, there existed for the first time in the hobby a central point for funneling data that would eventually be spread out once again to the aquarium community either in a revision or a new effort. The very abundance of this information rendered a simple revision out of the question. Thus, I have synthesized herein a completely new book on this marvelous group of intelligent fishes, and this time it is more than a simple summary of the family from the aquarium point of view. I have attempted to include as much scientific information as I could get my hands on, and you will see that something more than one week was involved! The present work represents almost a year of collecting and organizing material from diverse sources, and these sources will be cited in the Bibliography.

I hope you will enjoy this text as much as I enjoyed preparing it.

RJG

ACKNOWLEDGMENTS

I am greatly indebted to many people for help in the preparation of this work. Dr. Robert R. Miller of The University of Michigan read the section on *Cichlasoma*; Dr. James W. Atz of the American Museum of Natural History read the sections on *Geophagus* and allied genera and allowed me to examine the collection at the Museum; Dr. Dirk Thys van den Audenaerde of the Central African Museum (Tervuren, Belgium) supplied information on *Tilapia* and the cichlids of minor African lakes; Dr. Max Poll of the Central African Museum supplied a large number of rare papers on African cichlids, especially of Lake Tanganyika and the Congo basin; Mike Oliver provided information on lakes Malawi and Tanganyika; Hermann Meinken supplied much information on *Apistogramma* and allied fishes; Dr. George S. Myers and Paul V. Loiselle read much of the manuscript; and Irwin F. Simpkins of the Emory University Library worked above and beyond the call of duty in the pursuit of an enormous number of obscure or rare scientific papers. To all these gentlemen, I extend my deep appreciation.

Contents

DEDICATION

For my wife, Joyce.

1

Introduction

Cichlids are the most popular of all aquarium fishes, appealing to the beginner and accomplished aquarist alike. Their diversity of colors, shapes, sizes and behavioral patterns makes them an unlimited group in their potential to please any whim or requirement of all kinds of aquarists. Many of them are cheaply purchased. Those that remain expensive are nevertheless available to the serious aquarist who makes an effort to propagate one or a few types for purposes of trading. I received my first Lake Malawi cichlids in trade for a couple of old male killifish, bred and traded, and have yet to buy a single one for cash. I have traded killies for Lake Tanganyika cichlids, and have yet to buy one of these (still expensive) cichlids, though I am now breeding them and never expect to lay out a penny. *You can do this too.*

If your interests are strictly in cichlids, then invest in a group of young of a single but valuable species. Raise them, breed them, and trade them, and you too can have an outstanding collection for the price of your labors, and not because of your income. It is only when a pretty fish first arrives that its price is high. If you are patient, you can wait until others are propagating them and competing to sell them. If you are not patient, then make a small investment and treat yourself. Many cichlids are available for less than a dollar for juveniles, a few dollars for adult pairs, or perhaps fifty dollars for a pair of Rift Lake cichlids.

There are plenty of kinds for everyone, and everyone likes to trade. Almost all cichlids are easily propagated, and you can always find a taker for your fish who will have something you will want in trade. By all means, if you are a serious cichlid lover, you should be a member of the American Cichlid Association. Information on joining A.C.A. can be found in any issue of *Tropical Fish Hobbyist* magazine. Founded by Dick Stratton and Guy Jordan, its rolls now exceed one thousand.

About a thousand species of cichlids are known, mostly from Africa. The general distribution of the family Cichlidae is throughout Africa and outlying islands, along the southwestern Asian coast (one genus, *Etroplus*), and in the new world from mid-South America to Texas. Cichlids are not found naturally in Australia or most of Asia, and they do not occur in Europe.

A number of species have been intentionally or inadvertently introduced to American waters (Lachner, Robins and Courtenay, 1970). These include several species of *Tilapia, Astronotus ocellatus, Cichlasoma meeki, C. nigrofasciatum, C. severum, Cichla ocellaris, Hemichromis bimaculatus,* and *Aequidens portalegrensis.* Most of these have been introduced in southern Florida near commercial fish farms. Unfortunately some species have been introduced in the western states where they have made the status of several endangered killifishes even more precarious.

Etroplus maculatus, the orange chromide of Asia.

Cichlasoma nigrofasciatum, a common New World cichlid that now may be found in some waters of the United States, has not been determined to be ecologically destructive.

A number of fish and game agencies show remarkable concern for restricting the importation of exotic fishes because of the danger that such fishes may be released in native waters and compete with native centrarchids. These same agencies might show no hesitation about poisoning ponds and lakes containing unusual fishes, should some fishing group desire to introduce game fishes. In a number of cases the state agencies cloak protection of sportfishing in the jargon of the environmentalists, thereby confusing and obscuring the real issues of whether the environment or the fisherman is actually the concern of the agency. All too few agency heads, usually political appointees, will consult with resident ichthyologists or aquarium groups before taking action that affects devoteés of the hobby.

The disjunct distribution of the cichlids is worthy of a few remarks. First, the Asian representatives (*Etroplus*) are easily

The oscar, *Astronotus ocellatus,* is a South American cichlid which gives a dandy fight on a fly rod in Florida canals. Photo by Klaus Paysan.

Many species of *Tilapia* have been transplanted around the world as food fish because of their wide temperature and salinity tolerances and ready propagation. Photo by G. Marcuse.

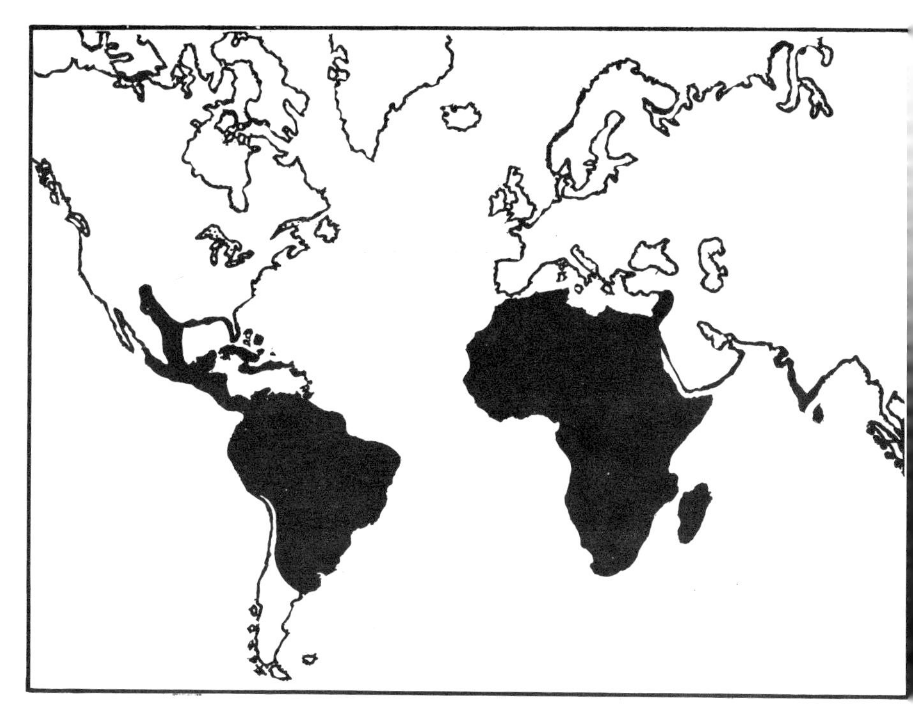

Geographic distribution of the family Cichlidae (black).

explained by assuming a *Tilapia*-like ancestor able to tolerate saline conditions (there are several such salt-tolerant species of *Tilapia* known today) expanding eastward along the coast bordering the northern limit of the Indian Ocean. Temperature and competition might have prevented these fishes from moving inland and colonizing the Asian mainland.

This is not to imply that *Etroplus* and its allies are an oddball group, or that *Tilapia* is more primitive than *Etroplus*. On the contrary, *Tilapia* is a modern genus and quite unlike primitive, ancestral cichlids. If anything might be said regarding the place of *Etroplus* and its allies in the course of evolution, it is this—that *Etroplus* and the cichlids of Madagascar are probably more closely related to ancestral cichlids than mainland forms on Africa. It is probable that the salt tolerance of *Etroplus*, *Paretroplus*, and other Madagascar fishes resulted in the colonization of the African land mass because *niches* (available space and food) were available. That they didn't succeed in Asia except on the periphery is probably because of the evolution of cyprinids in Asia, which must have taken up the very niches that were open in Africa. And although I have separated the treatments of *Etroplus* and Madagascar cichlids in this book, let the reader keep in mind that these forms are rather closely related and closer to the stem cichlid line than either the vast African or Neotropical faunas.

The vast cichlid faunas of Africa and the New World are of much more interest. Both the cichlids and the killifishes (family Cyprinodontidae) are found in both land masses, and the distribution of these families of fishes is only a part of the evidence for the theory of continental drift, a theory that is widely accepted today by scientists. Continental drift holds that South America and Africa were once joined as a single land mass, and many believe that the excellent match between continental shelves of the eastern hump of South America and the western gouge of Africa are not coincidental.

But if these continents were once joined, then how did they become separated? The answers are not entirely known, but one major item of importance is the Mid-Atlantic Ridge. This ridge is actually an enormous upwelling of mantle material extending through most of the middle of the Atlantic Ocean. This material is still upwelling and spreading and, as it increases in size, it is pushing the sea floor and the continents farther and farther apart. The age of this geologic feature and its rate of eastward-westward pushing are compatible with the distance of America and Africa and the probable time of divergence of the fish faunas, i.e., the cichlids and killies could well have already evolved before the land mass became divided. We are still in the dark concerning the nature of the forces creating this ridge in the middle Atlantic and no consensus has yet been reached. But we do believe that the South Atlantic basin, at least, is a young ocean; an ocean younger than a few of our families of fishes.

2

What cichlids are

To appreciate much of the literature on cichlids it is essential to have a basic knowledge of the evolution and variation of fishes, and this will also lead us into structural terms, many of which will already be familiar to all but the novice aquarist.

About 4.6 billion years ago the planet Earth came into being; whether as a mass of material shot out of the sun or as a collection of gases and detritus in solar orbit is not yet known. The Earth underwent physical evolution, with melting, solidifying, great upheavals and chemical changes. No later than 3.6 billion years ago the conditions finally were right for the formation of the first simple kinds of life. During the next billion years simple living things evolved in all kinds of diverse ways, thus laying the basis for the major lines we know today as the phyla of life.

At this point I will not try to draw a line between Animal and Plant Kingdoms, for this artificial division is a retrospective one and surely many intermediate kinds of living things have long vanished from the Earth. But certain worm-like and sea squirt-like animals did appear in the assemblage of life forms, and these were the ancestors of today's phylum of animals possessing a spinal cord down the back and certain other features. Many of these primitive Chordata did not give rise to more complex forms, but retained this basically simple anatomy, changing only slightly, and they are still with us today. Others of their cousins adapted to new opportunities and pressures and gave rise to small bulky animals covered with armor plate and having an oral opening plus an opening at the other end.

The first of these strange creatures is found in rocks of the Ordovician Period, about 500 million years ago. These armored sacs were known as ostracoderms, and their armor probably protected them from gigantic water scorpions of their day. But armor alone was not enough, and there was a tendency for elongation, loss of some of the heavy armor, and a tapering toward the rear. A skin flap appeared in some which may have been the origin of the functional tail or caudal fin. The ostracoderms were very successful and many kinds evolved. None of these jawless forms remain today, but a similar kind of animal would be the lamprey.

The ostracoderms were filter feeders, straining particles from the water through an increasingly complex gillraker apparatus (we think!), and sometime later in the Devonian era (about 350 million years ago) they were replaced by more complex fishes. The early ones were known as placoderms. These had paired fins, sometimes two pairs and sometimes as many as ten pairs! The placoderms evolved their forwardmost gill structures into jaws,

The Texas cichlid, *Cichlasoma cyanoguttatum*, is still evolving into various trophic (feeding) types in one region of northern Mexico. Photo by Laurence E. Perkins, F.Z.S.

Cichlasoma severum. Domestic golden strain. Photo by Curt Dunbar.

were still heavily armored up front, and were far more maneuverable than ostracoderms because of their fin development. The placoderms gave rise to separate lines of fishes, and one line is known as the teleosts or bony fishes. Other separate lines were the sharks and their allies, the lobe-finned fishes, and the lungfishes. Of course, some are more closely allied in evolution than others. The teleosts became surely the most successful vertebrate animals ever evolved. Their myriad species today fill oceans, lakes, rivers, underground pools, hot springs, and swamps; some of them are capable of soaring through the air, coming out on land, or even climbing partway up the roots of shoreline trees. They teem at the ocean's surface and prowl its blackest depths. And the fact that you and I have a pair of arms and a pair of legs is simply an accident of evolution that happened to have selective value as far back as the days of placoderms.

Earlier I pointed out that some placoderms had two pairs of paired fins while others had as many as ten. It just so happens that those with two pairs of paired fins were in the line of evolution leading to modern fishes (also with two pairs) and from early fishes to land animals. Thus, the pelvic (also called ventral) fins eventually became the legs of land animals and the pectoral fins became the arms (or forelegs) of land animals. In fact, the basic bone structure can be seen in the Devonian relict *Latimeria chalumnae* Smith, better known as the coelacanth.

Which brings us to the basic structure of fishes, and our discussion will center about bony fishes or teleosts. Fishes are generally bilaterally symmetrical and elongate, as this is the animal form associated with kinetic or motional activity. Sessile animals are often radially symmetrical (such as are sea anemones). Fish structures are either paired or medial. The skin is overlaid with scales, which are produced by the skin itself as an additional protective covering. These scales are arranged in an overlapping pattern, much like shingles on a roof, and their insertion is forward, thus allowing water to flow freely backward along the fish without running into pockets which might tend to work antagonistically to forward movement.

The scales may be cycloid (smoothly rounded) or they may be ctenoid at their rear edges (comb-like). Both kinds of scales are found in cichlids. But the skin does more than simply produce scales. There are gland cells in the skin that produce mucus, which forms a protective covering against disease organisms and enhances easy movement through the water, and there are glands that produce a fright substance.

Fright substance is released when the skin is broken, and tends to warn other fishes of the same or closely related species of danger in the area. There is some evidence that cichlids have such glands, but they are better known in other kinds of fishes. The skin also has pigment cells of various kinds which serve to give the fishes colors and patterns associated with the species, the state of anxiety, its level of sexual excitement, and many other behavioral and emotional states discussed under **Behavior.**

Along the midline of the fish are bony elements that extend out from the body and which are typically joined by thin membranes to one another. These are the unpaired or medial fins, and include the dorsal, anal, and caudal fins. The adipose fin is quite different in structure and doesn't occur in cichlids. Both paired and unpaired

Pterophyllum scalare, the angelfish, has been selectively bred to produce a great variety of different strains.

fins have a similar basic structure, but differ in their hook-up (or lack of it) to the body. The bony elements are the fin rays. They may be annulated (ringed) or not, but of more importance to us is whether they branch or they do not branch. Unbranched fin rays are often called spines, and are designated by Roman numerals, such as XII, indicating twelve of them. The branched rays (often called soft rays) are designated by Arabic numerals. Thus a dorsal fin count of twelve spines followed by six or seven soft rays would be designated XII/6-7. Sometimes a fish may have a stub of a ray at the front or rear of a fin, and this would be indicated with a small Roman numeral (i), ignored, or counted with the adjacent rays. Cichlids typically have spines followed by soft rays in the dorsal and anal fins, and only annulated rays in the caudal fin. Pectoral and pelvic rays are usually mostly soft, with or without a stub, and often a single pelvic spine.

Geophagus jurupari is a common South American mouthbrooding cichlid which attains a large size. Photo by Hilmar Hansen.

Cichlasoma festivum is a stately South American cichlid often found in the same waters with angelfish *(Pterophyllum scalare)*. This fine specimen was photographed by G. J. M. Timmerman.

Fishes hear (or feel vibration, the same as we do) by means of a nerve network set in the lateral line. This lateral line is actually a misnomer, as it often extends (and may be well-developed) on the cephalic (head) part of the fish. Typically, there are pores along the lateral line and on the head which lead down into sensitive pressure-receiving nerve terminations. Along the sides of the fish, these are seen as lateral line pores perforating certain scales of the fish. Typically, taxonomists will count the scales immediately above the lateral line. They may also count the vertical or oblique rows of scales along the whole side. In cichlids the lateral line is divided into a forward upper line and a rear lower one. By adding the scales above each part of the lateral line we may occasionally end up with more scales above the lateral line than total rows of scales, and this happens (rarely) when the upper and lower lateral lines overlap. Many fishes have reduced lateral lines, and then the total scales above the lateral line will be far less than the number of scale rows. Different systems of counting are useful for different kinds of fishes.

Vision in cichlids is well developed, and apparently they can see colors.

Fishes apparently can smell, but the relationship between taste and smell in fishes is close and beyond the scope of this book.

The lower jaw is called the mandible, and it is composed of a number of bones. The largest and forwardmost bone is called the dentary. Below and to the rear are other bones concerned with the hook-up of the dentary to the skull. There are teeth on the edges of the dentary, but we will cover them later. The pharyngeal teeth are important in cichlid taxonomy.

The upper jaw is far more complex. The upper jaw itself is made up of a forward premaxillary bone and lateral (to the side) maxillary bones. These too may have teeth. Many other bones are involved. The upper part or roof of the mouth is the palate, and it consists of a number of bones. These too may have teeth, but not in cichlids. Finally, there is a medial bone structure in the roof of the mouth that connects with the braincase, and as we shall see this is important in the classification of cichlids.

Steatocranus casuarius of the Congo River may look like a tough guy because of the frontal gibbosity, but he's really a pussycat.

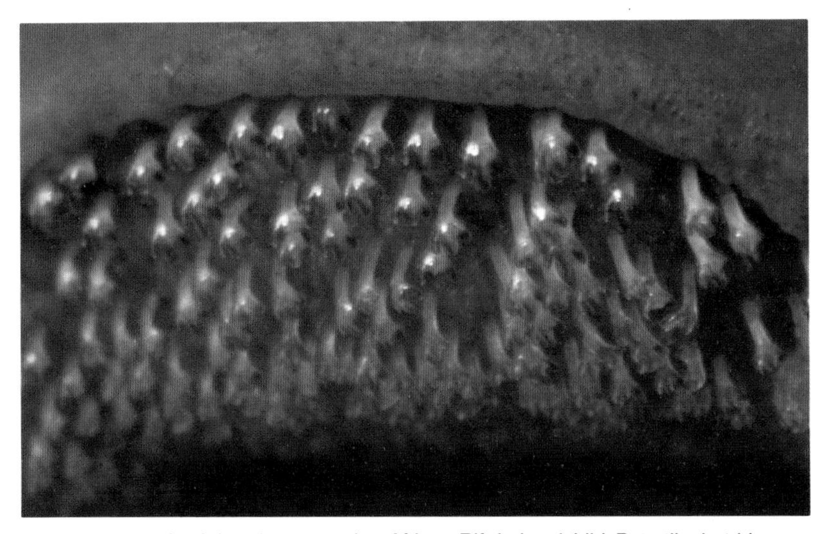

Tricuspid teeth of the algae-scraping African Rift Lake cichlid *Petrotilapia tridentiger.* Photo by Dr. Herbert R. Axelrod.

Teeth may attach to a number of mouth bones, and their number, shape, size, and distribution are all useful characters in ascertaining relationships as well as feeding habits. The tooth may be simple (conical), flattened like a shovel, bicuspid or tricuspid; and it may be curved, straight, long or short. The teeth may be sparse or crowded together, all the same or different in different parts of the mouth. There may be dog-like canine teeth on the sides of the lower jaw, or they may occur in such strange places as the middle of the upper or lower jaw. Canines are usually used for seizing or tearing, while spatulate (flattened) teeth may be used for scraping, and short, stubby teeth for chewing or grinding. Cichlids have a myriad of tooth types, and sometimes they use their teeth in ways that scientists find rather out of character.

American cichlids have a tendency to conical teeth (especially in *Cichlasoma*) and are not very exciting to a "tooth man." On the other hand the cichlids of the African rift lakes vary all over the spectrum in their tooth types, and from this point of view are quite interesting in their diversity and adaptations.

The head of a fish is typically covered with a number of armor plates all the way back to the gills. The gill cover is called the operculum, and other plates in the region are the preoperculum, the subopercle (I am using opercle and operculum interchangeably), and others. These plates may be smooth-edged, notched, or even serrated. The branchiostegals are a series of plates inside and below the operculum.

Gill structure is important in classification. The gill material is located on bony elements called gill arches (the forwardmost of which has become the upper and lower jaw). These arches often have structures on the end opposite the respiratory material (or gill filaments), and these structures are called gillrakers. In some fishes the rakers are highly developed and used for filter-feeding. In certain fishes, especially in America, there may be a lobe on the first gill arch, and it may project downward or in some other direction, be highly developed or barely apparent. In most cichlids, it is absent. The lobe's presence or absence and the number and distribution of the gillrakers are all important characters in classification, and a lot more important than fin ray counts.

The fin ray counts, and the lateral line (and other scale) counts are known as meristics. Of more importance are the relative body proportions of fishes, and these are known as morphometrics. Sometimes the relative proportions of structures change with size, and this is known as allometric growth. In general, one tries to describe fishes from a series of many sizes, presenting the range of variation for both meristic and morphometric characters. The total length of the fish is not a good criterion, as the caudal or tail fin of a museum specimen may be damaged or destroyed. Thus, a fish is measured to the base of its caudal fin, or the place from which the caudal fin rays first emanate. This is known as the standard length.

Morphometrics are usually given as percentages of the standard length, and/or (for head characters) the percentage of the head length. The head length is measured from the tip of the closed mouth in an oblique line to the rear edge of the operculum or gill cover. The snout length is from the same origin to the leading edge of the eye socket or orbit. The interorbit is the straight-line distance between orbits. All of these measurements must be made with calipers, and cannot be accurately computed from pictures.

Thus, we are now able to present a definition of the family Cichlidae as given by Jordan and Evermann (1898). Some of the terms we will not have covered in our general discussion, but these can be looked up in the glossary of any standard text, such as Randall's *Caribbean Reef Fishes,* available at most pet shops.

Pseudotropheus zebra of Lake Malawi, East Africa is a member of a group of recently evolved fishes which are classified primarily by dentition. Photo by D. Terver of the Nancy Aquarium, France.

Family CICHLIDAE

> Body elevated, oblong or elongate, covered with moderate sized scales, which are usually ctenoid; lateral line interrupted, usually ceasing opposite the posterior part of the dorsal, and then recommencing lower down on the caudal peduncle; mouth varying in size, terminal, the jaws with rather small teeth, which are usually conical, but sometimes lobate or incisor-like; no teeth on vomer or palatines; nostril single on each side; premaxillaries freely protractile; maxillary slipping under the broad preorbital; gill-rakers various; gill membranes often connected; dorsal fin single, with the spinous portion well developed, usually but not always longer than the soft portion; anal fin with three or more spines, the soft part similar to the soft dorsal; ventral fins thoracic, I/5; lower pharyngeal bones united into a triangular piece, with a median suture; branchiostegals five or six; no pseudobranchiae; gills four, a slit behind the fourth; vertebrae in more or less in-increased number, about 28 to 40; air bladder present. A large family of freshwater fishes of moderate or small size, representing as to form, size, appearance and habits, and even as to many details of structure, in the waters of South America, the Centrarchidae of the United States.

It must be remembered that Jordan and Evermann's definition was the result of work on bony fishes up to their day, and at present there are many more and diverse fishes known (particularly from Africa), which will tend to modify the older meaning of the term *usually* as used in the above definition. Branchiostegals are part of the gill cover apparatus, and the vomer and palatines are bones of the mouth cavity. The Centrarchidae are the American black basses and sunfishes.

The Family Cichlidae is contained in the Suborder Percoidei of the Order Perciformes (perch-like fishes) of the Superorder Acanthopterygii (spiny rayed fishes) of the Class Teleostomi (bony fishes) of the Subphylum Vertebrata of the Phylum Chordata. The cichlids are very closely related to the marine family Pomacentridae, differing principally in lacking a bony shelf at the orbit. Cichlids occur in the Americas from Texas southward well into South America, throughout Africa, and are represented by only three species of a single genus in Asia, *Etroplus*. New World cichlids are often referred to as neotropical, which is a biological, rather than merely geographic, zone.

3

Cichlid behavior

Cichlids are intelligent fishes. They learn to recognize the feeding container, the owner and other house occupants, and tend not to recognize strangers approaching the aquarium. Discrimination among persons develops with the age of the fishes, and is particularly marked among the deliberate neotropical forms, especially the larger species, than among some African lake forms. Thus our first reasonable generalization might be: *the larger neotropical cichlids are more likely to respond to human signals than the African forms, whether they be part of the* Haplochromis *species flocks or the* Tilapia *line of evolution.*

There are many examples in the aquarium literature of oscars and large *Cichlasoma* species behaving as family pets, going through hoops, etc. Certain species, notably discusfishes, may go through spawning and fry and egg protection in the presence of their owner, yet let a stranger enter the room and there is danger that the spawn may be eaten. Young fishes seem to be non-discriminatory to human signals, rushing to the front of the aquarium at the approach of anyone, in the anticipation that food is on the way.

The study of behavior is termed ethology, and the field of ethology is large, with persons entering from the realms of psychology and biology. Three types of behavior have been studied extensively in cichlid fishes: (1) reproductive behavior, (2) agonistic or aggressive behavior, and (3) behavior of fry. In the section of modes of reproduction in cichlids it is seen that all of these areas can overlap. And all of them have important survival value to the species.

The reproductive behavior of cichlids is treated elsewhere in this book, and differences occur in many groups. Thus, the pair bond in substratum brooders is generally strong and long-lasting, while in mouthbrooders it is generally of short duration. This brings us to the entrenched but incorrect notion of *mated pairs.*

Cichlids do not mate for life. They mate for the purposes of a single spawning. If they are still compatible when both are ready to spawn again, then they will again mate. But if one of a pair dies or is otherwise separated from its mate, the survivor will very likely accept a new mate if both are in good condition, timed relatively closely to each other, and somewhat equally matched. Even if the pair is *not* separated, but allowed to remain in a community aquarium, mates may be shuffled around for different spawnings. In short, cichlids are not Puritans. They are not, incidentally, swingers either!

While a pair is preparing to spawn or in the process of raising a family, their interests are toward each other and in the spawn, and not directed in any friendly way with other fishes. Occasionally a family quarrel ensues and one of a pair is killed or driven off.

Hemihaplochromis multicolor of the Nile River is a maternal mouthbrooder. Note the lower jaw distended with eggs in this female. Photo by Ruda Zukal.

Cichlasoma severum, golden strain, locking jaws possibly as a pre-spawning maneuver. Photo by Dr. Allen Shealy.

This is not due to a third party, but simply antisocial behavior probably generated by the desire for the territory becoming greater than the willingness to share it. Under natural conditions it may be that the male (usually) is expected to stay far off from the spawn and guard a rather extensive territory much larger than is available in the aquarium, and the female (usually) is expected to guard an area for the fry smaller, but nonetheless encompassing the region to which her mate is restricted under artificial conditions. Sometimes the female of a pair is killed by her mate, but this usually occurs before the female is responsive to pre-spawning signals. And so she may be killed (in the aquarium, but not in nature) either because she is not ready while the male is, or the male is not ready either and is solely interested in defending his territory.

Thus, the mated pair concept is a myth, implying only a compatible pair which can be predicted, with reasonable certainty, to accept one another regularly for purposes of sharing territory for spawning.

Agonistic behavior takes many forms. Generally, cichlids may be regarded as pugnacious fishes. This pugnacity is rooted in their territoriality. The fish will fight for what it regards as its own. Some cichlids have very limited territorial demands, and angelfishes may be content to guard a half of a twenty gallon aquarium, or some dwarf cichlids may be content to protect less than a square foot of tank bottom. Others have extensive demands, and a male *Pseudotropheus auratus* in a fifty gallon aquarium may kill any other male in the tank, if he has a mind to do so. The Lake Tanganyikan *Telmatochromis temporalis* may want to occupy all the rock piles in his tank, or he may accept the defense of only one. The Congo River form *Leptotilapia tinanti* will usually regard the entire aquarium bottom (of any reasonably large tank) as its own and vigorously drive off all intruders of its own or other species.

Leptotilapia tinanti of West Africa's Congo River is fearlessly territorial and will take over an entire tank bottom.

Lamprologus attenuatus, fighting males. Note the extension of the branchiostegals to magnify head size.

In general, cichlids tend to be aggressive to other fishes in the following descending order: own sex of own species—own sex of closely related species—own species—closely related species—distantly related species. Notice that the early portions of this order of descending aggressive habits are based more on behavioral than biological similarities. And this aggressive or agonistic behavior is dependent on the environment. Cichlids, like people, will get along until something bugs them. They have the innate ability to produce agonistic behavior (and other kinds of behavior), but this doesn't show up until they are stimulated in some way. The stimulus is called the releaser, and a simple example would be the presence of another male moving into a first male's territory, thus releasing aggressive behavior in the first male. If the second male wants to make a fight of it, he continues to produce other releasers (spread gills and erect fins, lateral weaving, etc.), and this releases greater and greater agonistic behavioral responses in the first male.

Reproductive behavior depends on a whole sequence of releasers, and in many cases these new stages of behavior mask other behavioral traits (such as propensity for being frightened by someone in the room, or by a larger fish in the aquarium), and may also be self-stimulating. Thus, fishes getting ready to spawn in one aquarium might be moved to a second aquarium, and this disruption is not adequate to keep them from following through and spawning.

The presence of danger or lack of light may release protective behavior in parent fishes, where a mouthbrooder will pick up its fry or a substratum brooder will collect them down below the parent in a compact mass. This type of behavior is shared between parent and offspring. The parent mouthbrooder may simply open its mouth, exposing a dark hole, and the fry will recognize this as a signal to enter. The parent dwarf cichlid may simply twitch its fins and shake its head, and this tells the fry to come on home. On the other hand, there may be no great danger, and the brooder may not signal the fry but instead chase them all over the tank to gather them for one purpose or another. This is most often seen in the early days of life, and suggests that fry responses to the parent may be learned rather than innate. Such an interpretation is very satisfying to the cichlid breeder who considers his fishes more intelligent than some of his personal friends, and certainly more so than his neighbors! Simple physical explanations may be fine for the African Violet set, but *our fishes can think!*

In the aquarium certain conditions may exist which destroy all chance of releasing a certain kind of behavior. In the pet shop, for example, a tank may contain a very large number of one species of fish. In this case no attempt is made to establish territories and agonistic behavior is at a minimum. Yet take three or four home and place them in a twenty gallon tank, and before you know it they are all fighting over the best corners and the best rocks and plants, in an effort to define territories. On the other hand certain behavioral traits may not be masked. A frequent observation by dedicated shop-hoppers is the finding of a tankful of rams (*Apistogramma ramirezi*) divided into spawning pairs, each pair with its own pit, having a grand old time under tenement conditions. It is likely that these fishes had begun prenuptial behavior at their Florida fish farm nurseries, and movement and crowding

Apistogramma ramirezi is a common dwarf cichlid that can be bred in small tanks. Photo by Dr. Herbert R. Axelrod.

Apistogramma reitzigi has been studied behaviorally and is not difficult to breed. Unfortunately, it is uncommon in the United States. Photo by Stanislav Frank.

could not turn them off. Perhaps at this time the only releasers to which they could respond were those provided by their mates, or any member of the opposite sex.

We have talked of behavioral releasers largely in terms of body movements. Coloration and patterns play an important role as well. *Apistogramma reitzigi*, a little-seen dwarf cichlid, has been extensively studied and is known to have a whole gamut of body patterns which are thought to provide distinct releasing signals. The female *Nannacara anomala* has been well-studied in Germany. The checkerboard pattern of the brooding female (not seen in the non-brooding female) serves as a warning to area intruders and may also serve for fry orientation. Many Central American *Cichlasoma* species alter their patterns with some degree of interspecific continuity; for example, a common pattern among

A species of *Haplochromis* from East Africa. The fish shown may be *H. burtoni*, but only laboratory studies could determine its identity. Photo by Hilmar Hansen.

Nannacara anomala, female in brooding pattern with eggs. Photo by Ruda Zukal.

frightened fishes is a series of vertical bands across the flanks, while when in fine fettle these bands may be reduced to minor lateral blotches. The banding resembles the juvenile pattern and perhaps is a mechanism to tell stronger fish that the frightened one shouldn't be considered a threat, or a competitor for space. In other words, it is a signal of appeasement.

Coloration changes mean different things in American and in African cichlids. In American cichlids it often means simply that the fish is mature, and there is no great increase in coloration from the inception of prenuptial behavior through breeding and rearing the fry. But in some of the *Haplochromis*-derivatives of the Great Rift Valley Lakes of East Africa, there may be two stages of color intensification. The first indicates that the fish is mature and guarding a territory, and the second is reserved for the brief courtship and mating ritual. This is best seen in *Pseudotropheus zebra,* a commonly available Lake Malawi species. Non-territorial males may be as gray as females, but territorial males become a rich deep blue with prominent vertical dark bands (again a difference in signal function from the Central American species). When spawning, the color may change to a light powder blue with greater definition of the dark bands. The closely related *Pseudotropheus auratus* does not have a two-stage color change. Non-territorial males may resemble females, but males that are either territorial or breeding have about the same coloration intensity, based on color reversal from the female or juvenile condition.

Pseudotropheus zebra of Lake Malawi. Mottled female and common blue-form male. Photos by D. Terver at Nancy Aquarium, France.

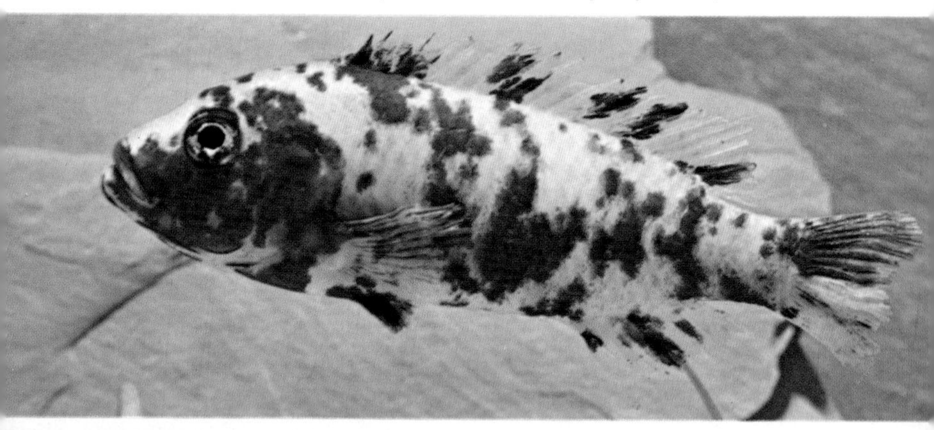

One of the mbuna cichlids of Lake Malawi, a female *Pseudotropheus auratus*. Photo by Dr. Herbert R. Axelrod.

All of these behavioral changes in coloration, pattern, and body movements have not evolved to entertain aquarists. They are adaptions to situations likely to occur in the fish's natural environment. The aquarist must learn to recognize these signals if he is to anticipate good news or bad, and a failure to provide an environment *to which the fish is able to relate behaviorally* often leads to damage or death. Thus, Central American cichlids are not good mixers with African cichlids. They may ignore one another (and that is fine), but they may also be unable to communicate their positions on who holds what territory, who wants to pick a fight, and (most importantly) who is signaling that he gives up. Remember that vertical banding in Central American cichlids often means appeasement and this same pattern in some mbuna means aggression. We want to avoid the situation where we have a failure to communicate.

The major nuptial behavioral motion of neotropical cichlids toward their mates is the rigid body, erect fins, and head flick. (Jaw-locking is agonistic and not mating behavior). To an African cichlid this may be meaningless. Males display to females among the mouthbrooding forms by arching their bodies and trembling or half-weaving at an eye-blurring speed. To a neotropical cichlid this is meaningless. A slow lateral weave with tail beating may be a universal signal of agonistic behavior, but neotropical cichlids take some time to respond whereas African cichlids seem to respond at much greater rates. In short, the activity of the average East African lake cichlid compared with that of the neotropical cichlid may be analogous to playing a 33 rpm record at 45 rpm. And again, the *rate* of response to a releaser may be as important as the nature of the releaser. Please keep in mind that these are all generalizations, and numerous exceptions will be found. Sometimes one must generalize and be emphatic to the point of inaccuracy in order to develop a principle, and it is principles with which we are here concerned.

Now everything I have said may be considered as half-truths, at best. The reason for this qualification is that the discussion has so far considered only the sense of sight (coloration, pattern and body movements). There are also the senses of smell, taste (which are closely allied in fishes and may be about the same thing), and hearing (via receipt of vibrations by the sensory endings of the

Lamprologus elongatus of Lake Tanganyika. Photo by Dr. R. J. Goldstein.

A large pair of *Astronotus ocellatus* yawning. See text for explanation. Photo by Jukka Jarvi.

lateral line nerves). We often say that a fish hears with its lateral line, and therefore its "ears" are on its flanks. This is not wholly true. The lateral line extends onto the head of the fish and, indeed, this frontal or cephalic lateral line may be very well developed, even when the lateral line of the flanks is very much reduced.

Sound consists of vibrations passing through a medium. In the gaseous medium of air, sound travels less efficiently than in the denser medium of water. We know very little of sound communication among cichlids, but Myrberg, Kramer and Heinecke (1965) have shown its significance in cichlid behavior. Taste and smell are also socially important in mate and sex recognition, and in fry recognition, but all of these considerations are difficult for the aquarist to recognize and record.

A frequent observation by aquarists is referred to as "yawning" in fishes. This has not been studied in cichlids, but it has been studied in other fishes as well as birds and mammals. It is pointed out elsewhere in this book that cichlids are very much like certain marine fishes. A recent paper (Rasa, 1971) discusses the yawning of the marine jewel fish or yellowtail damsel, *Microspathodon chrysurus*. Rasa concluded from her experiments that yawning can

Tilapia mossambica photographed at the Taronga Zoo, Sydney, Australia. Photo by Dr. Herbert R. Axelrod.

be initiated by high levels of excitement and low levels of activity. Further, it differs from yawning in birds and mammals in three ways. First, it is associated with increased activity rather than with sleepiness and relaxation of tension. Second, it doesn't appear to be related to breathing and oxygen-carbon dioxide variations in the brain. Third, it is not "infectious" in the behavioral sense; i.e., the yawn of one individual fish does not induce yawning in others. I suppose one might compare fish yawning with an isometric exercise or sitting down while swinging a leg back and forth. It is preparation for activity in the absence of any inducement to activity, as I interpret Rasa's discussion. Or to put it another way, it is a symptom of ants in the pants.

Another interesting aspect of fish behavior properly belongs under the section heading of reproductive behavior, but I will include it here for emphasis by separation. This is the use of a target fish to work off aggressive behavior by one of a pair of potential breeders. This idea is well known among aquarists, especially cichlid and anabantoid people, but it was first enunciated for me by Dr. James Atz of the American Museum of Natural History. Sometimes a pair of cichlids in its own aquarium

This plankton-feeding member of the Utaka group of *Haplochromis* of Lake Malawi has its protrusible mouth extended to form a sucking tube, as is present when the fish feeds on the zooplankton. Photo by Michael K. Oliver.

fails to breed, often because the male is too aggressive. In this case a third fish, usually of the same species or closely related, is placed in the tank to absorb the aggressions of the male, thereby taking pressure off the female and allowing formation of a closer pair bond, which often then leads to prenuptial and finally nuptial activity.

And so we can see that cichlid behavior falls into the categories of responses to their own and to other species, and there is not a single line of separation, but a gradation. Signals of aggression, of appeasement, and of danger in the vicinity, or signals of shoaling, etc., are easily seen by aquarists in terms of visual stimuli and responses, but there are other senses involved that we know little about.

Interpreting cichlid behavior simply on what we can see (*vis-a-vis* smell, taste, etc.), is akin to eavesdropping on a conversation in a foreign language, and only recognizing an occasional word. Sometimes you can get the gist of the feelings or attitudes of the parties, but it is easy to make a mistake unless you are fluent in the language. And just as people (all of one species) have different signals for the same messages, so may cichlids of a single species from different geographic areas. The different color forms of the Lake Malawi *Pseudotropheus zebra*, even though overlapping and often completely mingling in a single region, may perhaps be ethnic groups of the species. Who knows why these different color forms persist? The New Yorker's "*Jeez*", the Southerner's "*Shoot*", and the hippies' "*Oh, wow*" may all be different signals for the same statement. Why not in cichlids? And, as in people, it is not only what one says, but how one says it that, together, effectively releases responses in the recipient of the signals. Fish behavior is a big field and there is a large literature. But the literature is not massive, and there is much more yet to be done. This is a wide open research area.

Other aspects of cichlid behavior that have been studied in depth include digging movements (Heiligenberg, 1965*a*), and the suppression of certain activities by fright stimuli (Heiligenberg, 1965*c*). Sound production was studied by Myrberg, Kramer and Heinecke (1965).

4

Modes of reproduction in cichlids

Cichlids are adapted to a restricted variety of reproductive types, ranging from substratum brooding with little parental protection through similar brooding with vigorous protection, all the way to mouthbrooding types, where either the male or female, or both, incubate the eggs through hatching and yolk resorption, until the fry are able to fend for themselves.

All cichlids are oviparous, and none of them engages in primitive egg-scattering or specialized bubblenest construction. Typically, one or both parents engage in some degree of protective behavior, and this is unrelated to the size of the spawns. Thus, while it is an adage in biology that the greater the number of eggs produced, the less the protection (as in the egg-scattering codfish), different cichlids might produce from twenty to a thousand fry in a spawning and those with large spawns (such as *Hemichromis fasciatus* B) may be among the most diligent parents. The adage is probably valid as a generalization for higher categories, but within the family Cichlidae it breaks down.

The first step in reproductive activity is, of course, maturation of the individual fishes. Maturation here is considered to consist of two distinct components: (1) sexual decision, and (2) sexual maturity. Size is irrelevant to maturity, and depends on environmental factors such as oxygen availability, food supply, crowding effects (related to growth-inhibiting substances, still not clearly understood), and temperature (which in turn influences oxygen saturation of the water, and metabolic rate). Stunted, but mature, fishes are known not only in aquaria but in nature as well. For example, in attempts to populate African lakes and ponds with species of *Tilapia* as food sources, and to populate American closed waters with game fishes, it has been repeatedly observed that the fishes tend to reproduce to a point where they self-limit their own mature sizes. This has been most unfortunate in Africa where fish introductions are important to the nutrition of the local people, rather than to their pleasures. Lakes and ponds overgrow with huge populations of mature, but very small, fishes not suitable for consumption. This problem has since been solved

Pelvicachromis cf. *pulcher* of West Africa is larger and more beautiful than the common *P. pulcher* ("kribensis"). Female on right. Photo by Karl Knaack.

Members of the genus *Haplochromis* have well-developed ocelli or "egg-spots" on the anal fin. This specimen is either *H. burtoni* or a member of the *H. bloyetti* complex. Photo by S. Frank.

by introducing males of one species with females of another. The resultant hybrids are infertile, unable to overpopulate the waters, and reach sizes suitable for human consumption. In the home aquarium the only real advantage to large size is that the spawns will tend to be proportionally larger.

The chemistry of the water, at least in some fishes, plays a role in sex determination. It is well-known, for example, that species of *Pelvicachromis* will produce spawns largely of males or of females at different pH values. The nature of this sex determining mechanism is not known. It may be due to differential effects on sperm cells carrying either an X or a Y chromosome. In the Lake Malawi mbuna complex of *Haplochromis*-derivatives, young fish will show both sperm cell precursors and egg cell precursors, yet as they mature they become one or the other sex and do not reverse sex with increasing age (as in some non-cichlid fishes). In the same group of fishes, we find that hybrids are sometimes viable, form both sexes (rather than all sterile males), and are even fertile. In both hybrids and in normal fishes, maturity is a slow process and related to age; it cannot be speeded up by forced growth.

This brings us to the next phase of reproductive behavior, and that is the formation of the pair bond. But have we moved too fast? Is the pair bond an automatic part of growing up? Or does it have some more basic, underlying causes? Traditionally the formation of the pair bond has been studied working with mature fishes, and in the section on the genus *Etroplus* of Asia, it is shown that pair bond formation is an outgrowth of aggressive behavior. I would now like to go back even further to the predictable chagrin of animal psychologists, and present my own thinking and observations (totally without formal experimental data) on the evolution of pairing within a generation.

Cichlid fry tend to school (more properly, "shoal"), and do not define territories, other than home signals provided by one or both protective parents. Shoaling behavior is an adaption, in more primitive fishes, to the ravages of predation. There is safety in numbers. A predator finds it difficult to know which way a group will turn, or how it will react to a chase, and in much of the animal kingdom the predator solves the problem by cutting a straggler (or any other member of the group) out of the pack. Now, the

Etroplus maculatus of Asia, with fry. This species of cichlid has been studied almost as much as the New World *Cichlasoma nigrofasciatum* and *C. octofasciatum*. In the case of *Etroplus*, the fry respond to head flicks and feed on mucus on the flanks of the parents. Photo by G. Marcuse.

Cichlasoma cyanoguttatum of Mexico and Texas with their fry. This is the only truly native American cichlid. Other species have been introduced into American waters. Photo by G. Marcuse.

predator can focus its entire attention on the single prey, anticipate its moves after little observation, and plan its attack to either cut off the prey or force it into a blind alley.

Baby cichlids tend to group together for feeding activity (which is most of their activity), but this shoaling behavior is very weak. Hence there is the need for at least one parent to ride herd on the group and bring back strays from the pack. This togetherness is reinforced by certain parental markings. For example, the fry will largely tend to recognize and orient to a dark area, whether this be the mouth of a mouthbrooding parent, or an ocellus on the peduncle, flank or dorsal fin. This dark spot reinforces the inherently weak shoaling behavior. Soon after the end of parental protection, the shoal is on its own. There is considerable breakup of the group, with some individuals going their own ways. But many of the individuals continue to stay together in groups, and whether this is simply the use of common feeding grounds, common safe territory, or learned (or innate) shoaling is not clear, and may have different explanations with different species in different circumstances. See Myers (1960).

Apistogramma kleei, a dwarf cichlid of the New World. Photo by Karl Knaack.

At some stage in life, often (but not always) before the onset of maturity, certain individuals will remain fixed within a limited area of their environment, venturing short distances from a point. This would be the individual's home range, and is a common occurrence in bottom brooding fishes, as well as other fishes. Under conditions of crowding, where other individuals are venturing too close to that part of the home range considered home base (which may be an area several feet in diameter for even a small species), the occupant of the base may venture forth to chase the intruder from its area. This area is now its territory, and this is smaller than its range.

The territory is usually identified (by the fish) in terms of physical structures, such as the shoreline, rocks, logs, or plants. Or it may be limited by the edge of some other fish's territory. At any rate, once the protected area is defended, it can be regarded as a territory. In general, cichlids are territorial fishes. There are numerous exceptions. For example, many species of *Tilapia* occupy open waters where they feed in groups (shoals) on plankton

Cichlasoma meeki, the firemouth of Mexico, spreading its branchiostegals as it defends its territory. Named in honor of Dr. Seth E. Meek, late and great ichthyologist of the Field Columbian Museum of Chicago. Photo by G. Marcuse.

and larger materials. We can assume that fishes of the shoreline or of the bottom occupy established territories, while open water forms do not, during much of their lives.

Protection of the territory from intruders takes many forms. Typically there is a charge toward the intruder, with gill plates flared wide in order to make the defender seem larger than life. This may be followed by lateral weaving, side to side, fins fully erect, again to increase the illusory size and to signal to the intruder to get out or take the consequences. Tail-beating is the next step in the increasingly aggressive behavior. If the intruder doesn't respond to these signals, the aggressive behavior will continue to increase, with the fish butting the adversary with mouth closed. If this doesn't work, the mouth may then be opened, exposing the teeth. Finally, the defender may vigorously tear into the intruder removing scales, bits of fin, or even attacking the eyes. However, eye attacks are rare.

The intruder may consider itself an equal or better match, and respond with aggressive displays of its own. This usually releases more aggressive displays in the defender, and the two fish mutually react to release more and more aggressive signals. At some point, the usual situation is for one fish to give up. It may do this in many ways. First, it may simply flee with the defender hot on its tail until it is well clear of the territory. Or, it may signal appeasement by lowering or raising its head, clamping its fins, closing its gill covers, changing color or pattern, etc. This often terminates the attack, which must be constantly fed by releasers of aggressive behavior. All of these behavioral activities may occur well before the onset of maturity.

With maturation, territory defense may become more intense, but the fish now responds differently to the same or different signals. In the section on *Etroplus,* it is pointed out how the pair bond may form, with aggressive behavior going through a peace treaty, and terminating in the pair bond. Now two fish share a territory for the purposes of reproduction.

In many of the mouthbrooders, the pair bond is short-lived. The female enters the male's territory (if we are discussing female brooders), mating occurs following sexual display and excitement, and the female (now laden with fertilized eggs in her throat pouch), is driven out of the territory by the male who will shortly be ready to mate again with another female.

Male *Pseudotropheus auratus* in a cave that it has taken over as its territory. Photo by Dr. Herbert R. Axelrod.

The territory is actively defended against other fishes, especially another male. Photo by D. Terver of Nancy Aquarium, France.

In most of the substratum brooders, the pair bond lasts a long time, most often with the female guarding the spawn (eggs, and subsequently fry), and the male guarding the territory. The parents may switch roles at times, and in some fishes (notably certain species of *Tilapia, Chromidotilapia,* and *Geophagus*) there may be a degree of mouthbrooding following typical substratum brooding behavior. This mouthbrooding may be carried out by the male, or by both parents.

And so, whereas others have pointed out that the pair bond may be an outgrowth of aggressive defense of a territory, it seems clear to me that the establishment of a territory is not necessarily related to breeding, but is a more primitive type of behavior probably older than the one-to-one breeding activity of modern cichlids, and likely going back in time to the more primitive hypothetical group-spawning antecedents of the cichlids. (There is no firm evidence for such a group.)

Labidochromis species of Lake Malawi, a mouthbrooding cichlid. Photo by H. Hansen.

Female *Hemihaplochromis multicolor* with fry in her buccal pouch. You can see their irises glistening. Photo by Hilmar Hansen.

Thys (1970) has discussed the evolution of mouthbrooding in African cichlids. He points out that mouthbrooding habits arose independently and several times in African cichlids, but probably always from a basic stock which nested in large pits in the substratum (rather than fishes which attached their eggs to underwater structures such as rocks or logs). Associated with the pit nesting habit is the loss of egg structures for adhesion. With mouthbrooding, the egg shell or chorion became reduced in thickness and complexity, for it no longer had to withstand the ravages of a hostile environment; the mouth was a snug place to be.

In *Tilapia,* mouthbrooding arose at least four times in different lines of evolution, and most of the time the result was maternal mouthbrooding. Uniparental mouthbrooding did not necessarily arise from biparental mouthbrooding; in fact, in most species of *Tilapia* there has likely never been a biparental stage of evolution. Biparental and paternal brooding are probably specializations to certain conditions in the environment during evolution, but the maternal form of mouthbrooding was the common and most successful form.

It has long been thought that the mouthbrooding habit was a response to fluctuating lake levels, but many species of *Tilapia* are fluviatile (river fishes) and this is the *most* mouthbrooding river group there is! Also in African rivers, *Tylochromis* is probably a maternal mouthbrooder, *Chromidotilapia* is generally paternal or biparental, and river forms of *Haplochromis* are maternal. And so, the fluctuating lake level argument may not hold much water! It might apply if the river (fluviatile) fishes moved into lakes for spawning, or spawned with the advent of the dry season when the rivers were shrinking. But this is not likely.

Many African barbs and other fishes spawn with the advent of the rainy season, if they are at all seasonal. Certainly the fluctuating lake level hypothesis is valid in some cases, as in certain species of *Tilapia* in Lake Bosumtwi, and in some *Tilapia* of other lakes. In the subgenus *Sarotherodon* of the genus *Tilapia,* Thys suggests that mouthbrooding may be an adaption to open water life far out in a lake. In any case, we can have alternative situations where the fish first breed in a pit and hence the eggs tend to be non-adhesive. Near shore, where predators prowl or water levels might fluctuate,

Tylochromis lateralis of Lake Tanganyika. Photo by Gerhard Marcuse.

Tilapia mossambica, male in foreground. A new pink-gold-mottled strain has recently become available, but the wild type illustrated here is still a popular fish. Photo by Chvojka Milan.

the fry are moved from pit to pit, perhaps for cleaning (an aquarist's interpretation) or to confuse predators and keep them from learning the location of a spawn by multiple experiences, or to move the fish lakeward as the shoreline recedes with desiccation of the region. On the other hand it may be unsafe or unprofitable for an incubating fish to remain dangerously close to shore if the fish is adapted to pelagic life, and hence the eggs are picked up from the spawning site, wherever it is, and carried out to safe open water for incubation.

Clearly, mouthbrooding is an end that can have different causes, but why female brooding has predominated is an entirely different question in the rather sexually monochromatic species of *Tilapia* and the species flocks of the sexually dichromatic *Haplochromis* of the lakes. But before going into this question, let me qualify the statement about *Tilapia*.

Not all species are composed of similar males and females. Sometimes the differences in coloration or pattern may be quite marked, as in *T. mossambica*. Secondly, just because the sex differences in one group are great and those in another group are very minor is no reason to think that different mechanisms are at work. The question that comes to mind is: How much difference is *enough* difference? If a black spot on the chin or a red flush on the belly is sufficient to say what the fish needs to say, then is this any different than the gaudy differences between the sexes in the Lake Malawi mbuna *Pseudotropheus zebra*? I think not. Let us learn to recognize the existence of differences, and not be overly concerned with degrees of difference. You can be blunt or you can be subtle to make the same point, and which method you use depends largely on your audience. (This is not to imply that the mbuna are less intelligent than *Tilapia*, for their gaudiness implies something much more than mere sexual differences.)

Pseudotropheus auratus, female above, male below. These fish do not form long-term pair bonds but associate only for the act of spawning. Photo by W. Hoppe.

Pseudotropheus zebra, another of the mbuna cichlids of Lake Malawi. Photo by Dr. Herbert R. Axelrod.

In the special case of the mbuna, the great sexual dichromatism has another role, or perhaps several roles. It must be emphasized that the fishes in this lake have undergone recent explosive speciation. Because one male may breed with many females in the course of a season, that male's characters will contribute to the gene pool over time at a faster rate than in the situation where one male breeds with one female. Those males with the greatest amount of sexual releasers will get all the females, while those with less will have a lower and lower contribution to the gene pool over time. This helps speed up evolution. But there may be different kinds of sexual releasers, and different populations may choose different routes of female excitement. Evolution is proceeding so fast in Lake Malawi that some chromatically very different sibling species are kept apart (sexually) by coloration and behavior, and there has not yet been time for genetic isolation to keep pace with the formation of (behaviorally) biological species. Thus, in the aquarium *Pseudotropheus tropheops* has hybridized with *Pseudotropheus auratus* (when appropriate mates were not available for each species), and the hybrids were not only viable, but matured into both males and females, and these hybrids were fertile!

The pace of evolution has been tremendous. The fishes divided into trophic (feeding) types, but did not lose the ability to gain nourishment from foods (in the aquarium) that they normally did not consume in nature. Thus, many of our popular mbuna feed almost exclusively on plant material in nature, but attain excellent size and condition on an aquarium-provided meaty diet. Trophic specialization could then have been followed by coloration differences as ancestral males of a single trophic type utilized different sexual releasers to attract the females for breeding. This hypothesis does not explain what keeps females going to one type of colored male and not another, but the answer may be found in the situation in Lake Tanganyika. In that lake, Poll has reported that fishes tend to occupy the same region and the fauna of one rocky outcrop may remain rather different from that of a neighboring outcrop over the years. Perhaps the females are returning "home" for breeding, as are the young males, and this may reinforce evolution along one particular line. Because one outcrop can support only a limited number of male territories, the less successful (or weaker) males may be driven to new rocky regions where they form the nucleus of a new line by attracting females who stray here, rather than going directly home.

This hypothesis is weak, but its weakness is not equivalent to invalidation. What is logical is not necessarily true, and what is illogical often *is* true. Whatever the answers to the problems of sexual dimorphism and dichromatism, only the fishes know for sure.

Closely allied to reproduction is survival of the offspring, for the one is useless without the other. In almost all cases cichlid parents can be expected, in nature, to carry their offspring through the first days of free-swimming until the babies are able to fend for themselves. This means that their yolks are resorbed and their bodies are strong enough that they can now search out and consume environmental foods. In some cases a real family is formed, and the young remain with the parents much longer than would seem necessary under aquarium conditions. Yet in nature this behavior probably functions to protect the growing young from the ravages of predators until they are too large or too fast or too educated to make easy meals. It may also serve to reinforce species recognition, which may take a long time to learn well enough to be retained much later upon sexual maturity.

Baby discus *(Symphysodon)* feeding on mucus secreted from the skin of the parents. Photo by Gerhard Budich.

In the neotropical (American) cichlids, an interesting observation has been made, and this has also been well-studied in the Asian *Etroplus*. During most of the time, the fish has a uniform concentration of mucus cells in its skin. Around mating time, the concentration increases and the fish soon thereafter is capable of producing copious amounts of mucus. In *Etroplus* and in *Symphysodon* (the South American discusfish), the fry are seen to pick on the sides of the parents, feeding either on the mucus or on materials trapped in the mucus. Indeed, in *Symphysodon* it had long been virtually impossible to raise the fry after artificial incubation of the eggs, using the standard fares of brine shrimp nauplii or infusoria. It was Wolfsheimer who showed, many years ago, that the discus slime was necessary for raising the fry. Much later Friswold came up with a method for raising the fry without the parents, but this remained a secret except to those who got the information from him. But over the years, with much trial and error, a method was found independently by a number of aquarists and became common knowledge among

Etroplus maculatus in brilliant yellow color phase, with fry. Note the black pelvic fins. Photo by Ruda Zukal.

Etroplus maculatus is not as brilliantly colored when not in its brooding colors. Photo by Ruda Zukal.

discus fans. This method was eventually published (see the section on discusfishes) for the benefit of novices, and may not be too different from Friswold's method. Let me emphasize, however, that the similarity in end points does not necessarily indicate a single origin, but only weeding out from different directions.

The basic system includes the use of, at least, agar or some other indigestible binder, and egg yolk or some equivalent source of fat soluble vitamins and lipids (fats and oils). Perhaps the discus method will be the answer to the problem of raising marine fishes, which have been spawned a number of times, but raised very infrequently. Brine shrimp is a good source of carbohydrate and protein, but is low in fats. And fats and oils are important in development for proper nervous system formation. It just may be that discus fry, *Etroplus* fry (to a lesser extent) and many marine fry are released at a stage of nervous system development inferior to that reached by most cichlids. An analogy would be the comparison between marsupial mammals and placental mammals. The marsupial is born at an earlier stage of development and dependent on the mother to a far greater extent than the placental mammal. In the marine situation it may be the plankton, with its rich source of wax-containing copepods, which is necessary to provide fats or fat-soluble vitamins for proper nervous system development.

In any case, many cichlids show this increase in mucus cells, but in only a few cases is parental slime apparently necessary for the viability of the young. Mucus cells have not been studied in mouthbrooders, but as their fry become free-swimming at a late stage of development, and as the fry have not been observed to pick from the brooding parent(s), there probably is no great increase in the numbers of these cells. Why the discusfish, in particular, has specialized in this way toward what seems to be early release, is pure speculation at this time.

Sexual dimorphism, pair bonding and breeding have been studied by Wickler (1966a, 1966b). Parental recognition of young was discussed by Myrberg (1966), and drug effects on reproductive behavior were reported by Blüm and Fiedler (1965) and by Blüm (1968a, 1968b).

5

Breeding cichlids

The principles to be discussed in this section are geared to the interests of the "cichlidiot." The cichlidiot is a fanatic. He cannot be expected to (1) behave rationally when it comes to his hobby or (2) pay any attention to the non-spoken considerations normal people give to their wives and children. He'd rather watch his fish than the ball game, clean tanks than mow the lawn or fix the leaky tap, travel twenty miles to a fish friend's house than down to the corner for a bottle of milk, and move a hundred gallon tank than take out the garbage. He is also more likely to purchase this book than send his wife an anniversary card. Thus, I intend to discuss how the "cichlidiot" handles his fish room, and the novice will just have to decide for himself how small he wishes to start, and to what limits he is willing (or able) to go.

You can keep killifishes in a closet, but the "cichlidiot" needs a fish room. This can be a room in the house proper (where we plan to ruin the floor), or it can be (and ought to be) a section (only 90%) of the basement or garage. An outdoor pool is a supplement only, and that aspect will not be dwelt on here.

The room should be insulated to avoid the expense of a heater in every tank, and heat may be provided as needed by a fan-driven electric floor heater or a furnace if the basement or garage is used. The temperature should be maintained, for most species, at a comfortable level for the fishkeeper, or in the range of 70 to 85 degrees, with 75 being about right. A level concrete floor is best, and a drain and water tap source are recommended. If at all possible, try to have a tap with a single spigot giving an adjustable mixture of hot and cold, and have it threaded to accept a garden hose. An old section of hose should be handy for siphoning tanks, and it may be short for concrete floors (especially with drains) or long if it is needed to reach outside. If a basement is used, it is a good idea to whitewash the ceiling and walls to increase the light, and in any case light should be provided by sufficient overhead fluorescent fixtures. Tanks for dwarf cichlids may be planted, and these should have individual reflectors. Tanks for heat-loving cichlids, such as discus, should be provided with individual heaters. In general, tank covers are optional, and are recommended for rough adults, but not for fry tanks.

There are two goals to keep in mind. First, we want to limit our investment to the bare monetary minimum. Second, we want the hobby to pay for itself and its growth. These goals are part of the overall more important goal of mollifying the spouse.

Aeration ought to be abundantly available; one of the commercially available hatchery air pumps may be ordered through your local dealer. The prices of these units have now come down to where it is no longer necessary to build your own from a refrigerator compressor. By ordering air hose by the spool and valves by the dozens, you will effect considerable savings. Air stones are unnecessary; simply plug the end of the hose with foam rubber and weight it under a rock. The room should be equipped with your own private refrigerator-freezer (you can pick up a cheap

Clean water, good aeration and filtration, and one of a kind . . . the right combination for a healthy community of cichlids. In the foreground is *Cichlasoma managuense,* and behind is *Astronotus ocellatus.* Both are big New World species. Photo by Dr. Robert J. Goldstein.

The lack of plants is fairly obvious in this large aquarium set up for cichlids. Included are angelfish *(Pterophyllum scalare)* and flag cichlids *(Cichlasoma festivum)*. Photo by Dr. Herbert R. Axelrod.

unit from a junk dealer or a major appliance dealer who has lots of trade-ins), to keep your frozen and thawed foods.

You will have now three types of aquaria, (a) breeding tanks, (b) fry tanks, and (c) community tanks. These will be dealt with separately.

BREEDING TANKS

Ten gallon aquaria are sufficient for medium-sized cichlids and angels; larger tanks should be used for larger substratum brooders. The substratum brooders may be kept in pairs in bare tanks, with aeration, and a narrow rock, flowerpot chip, or strip of slate for receiving the eggs. If the fish spawn on the glass, you will be forced to leave the eggs with the parents, but if they spawn on any other material it is to your advantage to remove the eggs for artificial incubation. The narrow breeding substratum is chosen to fit into a wide-mouth gallon jug. This will be further discussed under **Care of Eggs and Fry,** below. You can also breed mouthbrooders by setting them up as pairs, but many people prefer to breed them in community tanks. The mouth-brooder breeding tank that will hold one male and one or two females ought to be set up with sufficient gravel and rock to allow the fish to construct caves. In this arrangement, plan to remove the egg-laden brooding female rather than (in the case of substratum brooders) the egg-laden hard substratum. In either case, the set-up of the aquarium assures that the eggs will likely be placed where they are easily removed from the breeding tank.

COMMUNITY TANKS

We have two kinds of community tanks; those set up to breed mouthbrooders of a particular lake (an all Malawi mbuna tank, for example), and those set up simply as holding aquaria. In either case the tanks should be as large as possible, and be loaded with rocks and gravel. Filtration should be provided from without, and live plants should not be used except as food. Avoid putting large pairs of neotropical cichlids in the same community tanks, as they may decide to set up housekeeping and beat the daylights out of the other tank inhabitants. If they want to breed, then give them their own private aquarium. If you don't want to breed them, then keep them in separate community tanks.

Pelvicachromis pulcher preparing to spawn in a flower pot. Female above, upside down. Photo by Ruda Zukal.

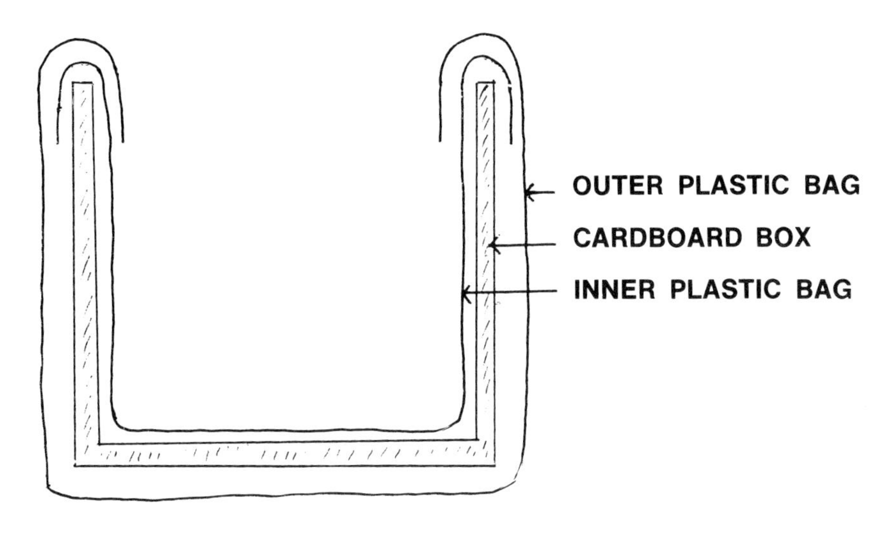

Construction of a fry tank. Drawing by Dr. R. J. Goldstein.

The value of large holding aquaria cannot be overstated. Quite often you will find, either in a shop or at a local fish club auction, a very large single specimen of a desirable fish. You can pick up this goody and then hope to find another sometime in the future. In this way you might pick up a valuable pair of fish for much less than you might think. Pairs are always far more expensive than singles, and you can expect that any male and female of the same species, if both are in good health and otherwise closcly matched, stand a good chance of breeding. But someone with a big single fish will practically give it away just to get rid of it.

FRY TANKS

Here is where you get into the big savings and make the hobby pay for itself. First of all, if eggs are removed from substratum brooders, they will spawn much more frequently than if they are allowed to raise their own families. And the more you raise and sell to local shops, for either cash or credit, the lower your costs in the hobby. But be sure to devote sufficient space to bread and butter species such as angels, which have about the best market of all. You'll have trouble unloading large quantities of ports

(Aequidens portalegrensis) or other less commerical fishes. The cheapest cichlid fry tank may be constructed of cardboard boxes and plastic trash can liners (see the drawing). Make sure the box is a snug fit for the bags, and drape the open edges of the bags over the rims. Aerate heavily.

Set up a bank of these fry tanks with sufficient overhead fluorescent light so that you can observe the fry and see the tank conditions at the bottom. Inside box filters are useful. Activated carbon and charcoal are optional. For filtering material you can use either dacron batting, glass wool (not recommended), or old panty hose with runs, that your wife is throwing out anyway. Weigh the filter box down with rocks or marble chips, available at a nursery.

Use plastic buckets, rather than the siphon, for removing water. You can add water with the garden hose to the tap, as for your other tanks. You can force growth on your fry using a

Aequidens portalegrensis, also known as the port cichlid or the black acara, is an easy fish to breed. It has little commercial value and may be found occasionally in canals in southern Florida. Photo by H. Hansen

A species of *Tilapia* introduced in Indonesia. Photo by Dr. Herbert R. Axelrod.

combination of much space, frequent water changes, and heavy feeding. Use snails or goldfish as scavengers. Avoid sharp-spined catfishes in these plastic lined containers.

Alternative containers may be made from kiddie pools (if they do not have a strong smell of vinyl), old refrigerator liners with all chips and bolts carefully covered with a neutral silicon compound, or plastic homemade pools which can be made by buying a roll of construction plastic at any building supply store. Use a corner of the basement as two walls (do not attempt this on a wooden floor!), and set up some styrofoam boxes (from your local dealer) as the other two walls (see the drawing). Fill the boxes with water to keep them heavy (and you can put a pair of dwarf cichlids in each box if you wish), and line the area within this wall-plus-box frame with the sheet plastic. The pool will be shallow, but it can be extensive, giving you a great surface to volume ratio. Such pools are not very good for large cichlids because of the need for sharp-edged broken flowerpots, and rocks; the spines of larger fishes might puncture the plastic during a chase into a corner.

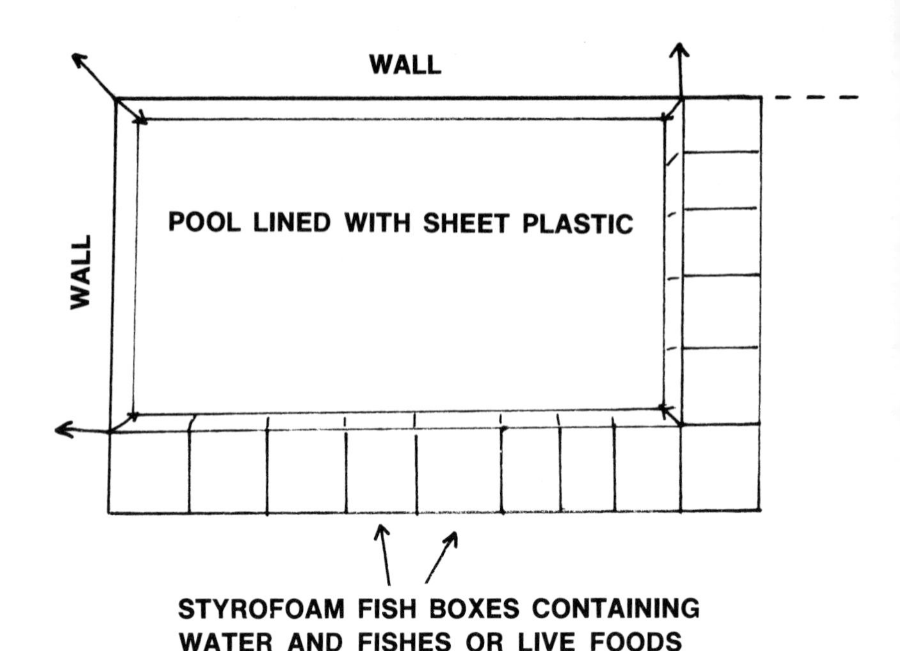

Construction of a plastic-lined pool. Drawing by Dr. R. J. Goldstein.

CARE OF EGGS AND FRY

A female mouthbrooder should be removed from the tank in which she spawned (whether community or smaller), and placed in a ten or more gallon tank with caves, rocks, and plants. Plants are advisable and this tank should be individually illuminated, but not too brightly. The tank should be filtered or aerated and the water kept immaculately clean. Some mouthbrooders will eat while brooding, but feeding is not necessary. If you must feed, then use live foods only. Keep only one brooding female in a tank, as this is a period of belligerence, and a newcomer may be badly beaten. If the female drops the eggs, and you think they might still be viable, pick them up and suspend them in a net near a current of water, keeping the water hard, somewhat alkaline, and darkened. Above all, handle all eggs with clean, warm water.

If the substratum brooders have cooperated by depositing the spawn on the narrow substratum you have provided, remove this slate or rock and place it in a wide-mouth gallon jar or plastic

Tilapia mossambica, breeding. The sperm tube of the male is visible in this photograph. The female is picking up eggs she has just spawned. Note her swollen jaws. The fish are spawning in a depression in the sand which should not be considered a nest but simply a spawning site. Photo by Chvojka Milan.

If *Tilapia mossambica* has any nest at all, it is the throat of the female. Here is where the eggs are incubated and the babies kept until they can begin to fend for themselves. Photo by G. Marcuse.

bucket with water from the breeding tank. This water should be heavily darkened with methylene blue, kept warm by raising it off the floor or inserting it in a large, heated container. Illumination should be kept to a minimum. Gentle aeration next to, but not on, the eggs is very desirable. For darkness an individual jar may be placed inside a large paper sack from the grocery store. After a day or two, some of the methylene blue dye will be adsorbed by the rocky material, and more should be added until hatching. Some of the eggs may fungus, and these can be left alone or removed with an eyedropper and toothpick. If the fungus patches become extensive, then squirt the fry off the rock with the eyedropper and remove the dead material and the rock. At warm temperatures hatching usually occurs within three to six days (sometimes less), and the fry will shortly scoot around over the bottom. Begin feeding newly hatched live brine shrimp nauplii when the fry begin swimming, and when the fry seem strong (in a few more days), pour off most of the jar water and transfer the remainder with the fry into one of your large growing tanks, such as the plastic bag-lined cardboard box.

A very simple spawning set-up for this pair of Wong's golden angelfish. The slate rests on a wire holder in a bare tank. Photo by Peter Wong.

These angelfish have spawned on the slate, the eggs clearly visible in this photograph. Photo by Peter Wong.

In a short time the young angelfish start to develop the elongate dorsal and anal fins characteristic of this species. Photo by Peter Wong.

In the mouthbrooding tanks, the females will drop their fry in two to five weeks, depending on species and waters of origin. These fry will be strong. Remove the female to a recuperation tank for at least ten days, until she is strong and eating well. Only then may she be placed back where she came from, and be sure to rearrange the tank to destroy established territories. After a few days of feeding the fry, they too can be transferred into fry-raising tanks. Lift them out with a net.

GENERAL CARE OF ALL AQUARIUMS

Cichlids are not for lazy people. All of them, fry and adults, and of any species, appreciate frequent partial (but extensive) water changes. Hence the heavy use of the siphon, bucket and hose. Most cichlids do best in slightly alkaline water, but discus prefer it neutral to slightly acidic. Know the waters from whence your fishes hail, and try to set up their tanks accordingly. When in doubt, go alkaline, and avoid excessive heat.

FOODS

Adult cichlids, whether they eat plants or meats in nature, usually do best on a meaty diet in the aquarium. Frozen or live adult brine shrimp, scraped or blended beef heart, minnows, worms, crickets, roaches (not in *my* house!) and excess fry of other cichlids all make excellent foods. Flake foods are a good supplement. Trout chow is cheap and a good staple, but should be supplemented with live foods occasionally (at least once or twice a week). This subject will be elaborated upon separately.

6

Cichlid fry

We can assume that the basic cichlid type is a substratum brooder, and mouthbrooders are therefore specialized types that must be considered derivatives, irrespective of whether the specializations are simplifications (involving loss) or expansions (involving gain) of attributes.

The cichlid egg of the substratum brooder is generally small (about a millimeter or two), and enclosed within a complex chorionic membrane. This chorionic membrane is composed of a series of submembranes, and typically there are one to many filamentous extensions of the egg membrane which attach the egg to the substratum. This is best observed in those cichlids which choose a hard substratum, rather than those which choose a pit as the typical spawning site. Hypothetically, the harder the substratum the greater the tendency for the filaments to be reduced in number and more elongate and tougher. Unfortunately, there are insufficient data available to back up this contention. The logic stems from the following principles.

Pit spawners require no single strong filament to anchor the eggs, but there is an advantage for the eggs to be sticky, so that they tend to attach to one another in a cluster and thus be unlikely to be washed out of the nest by fleeting strong currents. Stickiness is best accomplished, as in killifishes, by numerous filaments. A single strong and elongate filament is seen in the eggs of the rock cave spawners of the African genera *Nanochromis* and *Pelvicachromis* (which are quite closely related). Many other species of cichlids known to spawn on a hard substratum appear to lack filament attachments, but this is usually superficial. Close examination will often reveal the presence of a single, strong, if short, filament.

In the mouthbrooders such stickiness of the eggs is obviously unnecessary and may even tend to interfere with oral circulation of the eggs, cleaning, etc., and such fishes are characterized by eggs having reduced membranes. The eggshell is thinner, and the threads are reduced or absent. With mouthbrooding there is also a tendency to larger and fewer eggs. Thus, in the Lake Malawi mbuna the eggs may be about three or four millimeters in diameter, and their number tends to vary (in aquaria) from very few up to about fifty or slightly more (with many exceptions known), based on the condition and size of the female.

In *Tropheus moorii* of Lake Tanganyika the eggs may number only up to ten or less, and they are huge, about seven millimeters in diameter. The adult fish itself is small, and the generalization should be observed in the perspective of adult fish size, size of eggs of related species which brood somewhat differently, and the various brooding types found in each particular habitat (river, lake, etc.). The eggs of the bottom-brooding *Telmatochromis* and *Lamprologus*, for example, are more numerous and smaller in size, yet these fishes are found in the same lake.

Telmatochromis temporalis, from Lake Tanganyika, East Africa. This bottom nester has distinctive markings but little coloration in the body and fins. Photo by Dr. R. J. Goldstein.

Tropheus moorii, also from Lake Tanganyika, is a highly specialized mouthbrooder. The eggs are few in number and among the largest known in the family Cichlidae. Photo by Dr. Herbert R. Axelrod.

With hatching, the fry of bottom type cichlids tend to attach to the substratum or each other by means of other sticky threads. These threads are products of special glands in the head. At about the time the yolk is resorbed by the developing juvenile, the glands deteriorate and disappear, the fry are strong enough to break the now tenuous attachment, and this transient phase terminates. Needless to say, head glands generally do not occur in mouthbrooders. Again, this is a specialization of the fry of substratum brooding types, and it is lost in the more recently evolved mouthbrooding types.

Cichlid fry, in addition, tend to develop one of two different patterns of dark pigment. This is best seen in substratum brooders, but is obscure in mouthbrooding types where the fry are released well into advanced development. In the substratum brooders, the fry tend to be either mottled or to possess a single horizontal dark band. Often these patterns are alternated in the early days of a single species. It is likely that the horizontal lined phase (at least) serves to hold the shoal together, i.e., it may be a releaser of shoaling behavior. It is found in many diverse species of cichlids and is generally retained for a long period. When the lined phase gives way to other patterns, the shoal tends to dis-

Tilapia mossambica, female with fry. At a signal from the mother, the fry will rapidly swarm into her mouth for protection. Photo by Chvojka Milan.

seminate its individuals. Again, many exceptions may be found under aquarium conditions where reinforcers of shoaling behavior (i.e., the presence of predators) may be absent. See Myers (1960).

The feeding and shoaling behavior of cichlid fry are covered elsewhere in this book, and will not be repeated here. Certain early stages of fry development were reported by Baker (1964), working with the Texas cichlid. See also Fishelson (1966) on mouthbrooder development and Dadzie (1968) on structure of the egg shell membranes.

Jones (1972) detailed the specific stages of development of several substratum-brooders. He noted that fry of substratum-brooders always have three pairs of adhesive organs. The fry of mouthbrooders have such glands also, but they are rudimentary.

7

Foods for cichlids

Cichlid fry do not require infusoria. Some species, notably the discus, can be hand-raised using special conditions. (See the section on discus for this information.) Otherwise, we are left with two other live foods, brine shrimp nauplii and microworms. Powdered or liquid fry preparations are not recommended. Microworms are not the live food of choice, as they are troublesome to maintain and probably less nourishing than brine shrimp. Microworms also have the annoying habit of finding their way into the gravel (if the tanks are set up that way), where the fry tend to follow them and become lodged, there to die. It is always a good idea to use bare bottoms in fry tanks, for you are going to feed heavily, and continually remove leftovers and wastes.

Microworms eat live yeast, and yeast feed on grains. When transferring a portion of an old culture to a new one, follow these procedures. First, the grain may be any flake baby cereal, such as Pablum or Gerber's, and I prefer the mixed grains to wholly wheat or wholly rice. It should be moistened to form a very thick paste. Loose mixtures are too wet and do not last very long. Place the thick glob in a clean container (mix it elsewhere) with a rather tight fitting lid having holes punched into it. This will cause the worms-to climb the walls toward the fresh air. Transfer about a half teaspoonful of old culture and lay it right on top of the pasty glob. Do not add more yeast. There will be plenty in the old culture, and if you add more yeast there is the danger that they will multiply much faster than the worms can feed on them; you will get a wet, slimy, smelly mess. When the worms stop climbing and the culture is getting very wet, it is time to make a new culture. Don't delay, or you are liable to lose the whole thing. For feeding, wipe the worms off the wall with your finger, and swirl your finger in the tank.

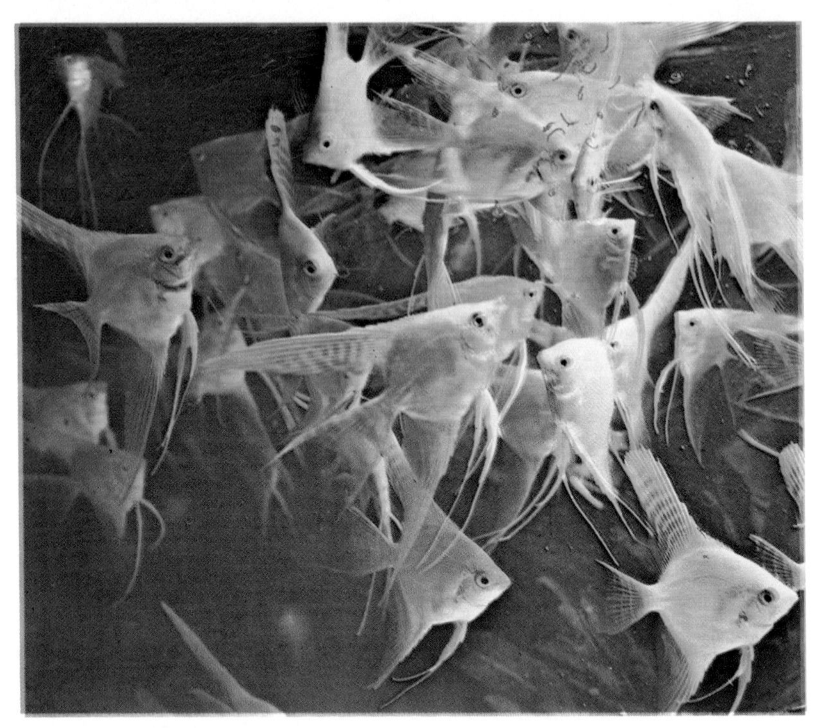

This mixed group of veiltail and non-veiltail angelfishes feed avidly on *Chironomus* larvae, popularly known as bloodworms. Photo by Peter Wong.

Brine shrimp nauplii are the food of choice. The larger the quantity of eggs purchased, the cheaper the price. I buy it by the gallon. Read the directions for hatching on the egg container, and then modify them in this way. For California eggs, expect 48 hours at 80 degrees for a complete hatch, and cut the salinity from eight to six tablespoonfuls of salt per gallon. Add half a teaspoonful of epsom salts. For Utah eggs, just follow the directions, and still expect 48 hours for a good hatch. Change your shrimp hatching water every other hatch or, preferably, every single hatch. Use rock salt, as it is cheap. Ice cream salt is about the same thing. Use a gallon jar with very heavy aeration, and preferably tip it so the eggs that fall tend to be carried into the air stream. More exotic containers can be made, but they are not worth the trouble.

Plastic brine shrimp cones are available commercially, and these make up in efficiency what they lack in volume. Their drawback is that they are very difficult to clean, whereas a gallon jar can be easily wiped inside with the palm of the hand. When 48 hours have gone by (and you should have at least two jars going all the time), remove the air line, and let the eggshells settle. Many of the shrimp will settle too, and this cannot be avoided. Look into the jar carefully from the side to be sure that the majority of shrimp are fully hatched. If the large majority are still hanging from their egg shells, then aerate longer. Assuming you have a good hatch and the shells have settled, place an old aquarium net rigged with a handkerchief (either attached to the frame or overlaying the commercial netting) on an empty bucket or jar. Slowly pour the water into the net, and the shrimp will be retained as the water passes through. Get as far down to the shells as you can, and if some shells get into the harvest don't worry about it. Pour out the dregs into a discard pail. Either throw away the hatching water or use it again *only* if it is neither smelly nor translucent.

A popular cichlid food, *Gambusia affinis* is common in the southeastern United States. Photo by Karl Knaack.

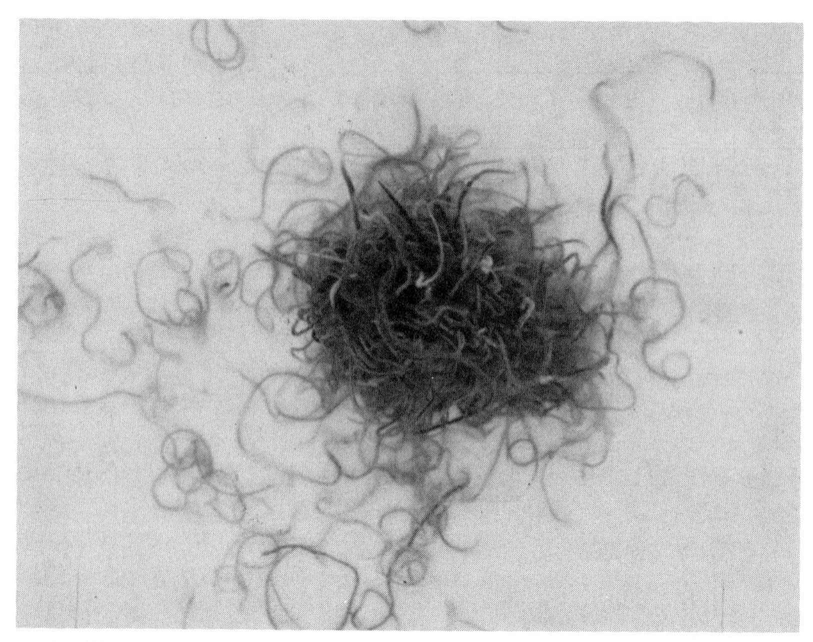

Small worms such as these tubifex worms will be greedily accepted by most cichlids. Photo by Dr. Cliff W. Emmens.

Invert the handkerchief containing the shrimp into a small glass or plastic box, and swirl and feed with an eyedropper for small tanks. Just swirl and pour for larger aquaria. Keep some salt in the fry tanks to help keep the shrimp alive as long as possible. Feed frequently; not less than once a day.

The eggs of brine shrimp require special care. In general they are not affected by temperature, so long as they are kept absolutely dry. In a dry state, they will last a year or more. Save the plastic cover that comes with the shrimp container. Open the container any way you must to remove small amounts of eggs at a time. I pour off several ounces into a small plastic container, and quickly reseal the large egg container with its plastic lid. The small container is used for the daily making up of fresh batches of eggs for hatching. Your fish room will be very humid, and it is a good idea to wrap some rice in a piece of old stocking, and place this in the small shrimp egg container to take up any moisture. Do not add salt grains, as this will have exactly the opposite effect, and you'll have a dead, wet mess.

Adults and juveniles past the fry stage can be fed a great variety of foods. In general the mouthbrooders enjoy some plant material in the diet. Duckweed is excellent and perfectly safe to use. Cooked spinach is permissible if fed in moderation, but it might foul the water if not all eaten.

Flake foods and trout chow are good foods. The former is very much more nutritious, but also more expensive. It is up to you which to use, if either. I recommend some flake food in the diet.

Minnows and wild fishes of other types are good foods for neotropical and some African cichlids. Generally, the mbuna will ignore them, and small sunfishes are at the bottom of the list of fishes likely to be eaten by cichlids. *Gambusia* are good food, but may escape many cichlids, having the tendency to hide in corners where they are unobserved. Minnows are best of all, hanging in the open water and easily caught. Even mbuna will sometimes eat them. *Cichlasoma* species love them. When bringing wild small fishes home for purposes of feeding, first place them in a gallon jar with aeration, and add four or five drops of formalin (the concentrated commercial material labeled 37% or 40% formaldehyde) to the gallon. This will kill the possibly present flukes

Larger worms, for example earthworms, may be chopped into bite-sized pieces for the bigger cichlids. Photo by P. Imgrund.

(gill parasites and skin parasites). Whether it will also kill fluke eggs (which hang by threads from the fishes' gills) is unknown. Store the bait fish in a separate tank from which you can remove them for feeding. Occasionally give them another exposure of formalin, at the same dosage, but in the holding tank.

Crushed snails make an excellent food, but do not use wild snails. These may carry worms which might infect your fishes with black spot or yellow grub metacercariae. Tank-raised snails are clean and recommended.

Earthworms are excellent food, and may be purchased, collected, or grown in your own backyard or basement. Feed them plenty of leaf mold, old bread, etc., and keep their container very wet. Tear them up before feeding if they are quite large. Small worms can be dropped in whole.

Tadpoles are virtually ignored by most fishes, and are thus not good food. They are, however, excellent scavengers and a lot

Aquarium snails can provide variety and nutriment in a cichlid diet. Photo by J. A. Cavalier.

The best food for most fish is, of course, fish . . . but this is going too far. Photo by Dr. Herbert R. Axelrod.

cleaner to keep than goldfish. Some large cichlids will eat them, so use your judgment and make observations when introducing them into a tank for any purpose.

Crickets and other insects and their larvae (such as mealworms) are good foods for such big fellows as oscars, but they can be sloppy to feed. Oscars, especially, have a tendency to grab, chew, spit, grab again, etc., and this can make quite a mess out of clean water.

Frozen brine shrimp, bloodworms (chironomid larvae), and other commercially available frozen foods can be rather expensive unless purchased in bulk. They are all good foods.

Sliced or blended freshwater mussels are nutritious, but most fishes do not care for them. Marine shellfish are eaten avidly.

Beefheart by itself is an excellent food, but some considerable trouble to prepare. Buy it in lots of ten pounds or more from the packing house, where the price will be half what it costs in the supermarket. Cut off all the stringy and tough parts, leaving only the soft meat. This will reduce the bulk to about half that with which you began. A very strong and sharp knife is necessary. You can now store it in the freezer and feed scrapings to your fishes, or you can blend it with water plus some salt, pack it in containers, and freeze it. Either scrape the frozen blend or let it thaw before feeding. Never throw large chunks of frozen food into a tank where the fishes are liable to gulp down these big icy and hard chunks.

Frozen mixtures can also be prepared. One of my favorites (because it is easy to make) consists of varying amounts of fish (fillets or whole small fishes), liver (any kind except pork, which is too fatty), and some Pablum or Gerber's baby food as a binder. For the B vitamin complex you can add a little bit of old microworm culture (reeking with yeast). Yeast synthesizes most of the B vitamins. In fact the odor of yeast is due to one of them, thiamine. For a source of D vitamins (modified carotenoids), add egg yolk, fish liver (or its oil), or plenty of green leafy material. The carotenoids will probably give your fish good color. If you throw in whole fish, then the fish liver is already in, and nothing more needs to be added. I blend this whole formulation and store it in the freezer. I also thaw before feeding, but others prefer to scrape and feed. Blended foods should always be fed cautiously, and additional water changes will be necessary. It is easy to acidify or foul a tank with such foods.

For fat absorption in *Tilapia* see Sivadas (1965). For carbohydrate metabolism see Liu, Krueger and Chih (1970). Liu *et al.* showed that glucose is largely oxidized via the efficient TCA cycle (66%), 19% via the pentose shunt, and 22% via glucuronate; the latter value is quite high.

Morris (1962, 1967) studied the relationships of oxygen, temperature, size, and adaptability in *Aequidens portalegrensis*. The endocrinology of *Cichlasoma octofasciatum* was studied by Mattheij et al. (1971).

8

Parasites of cichlids

Cichlids will succumb to many of the diseases that plague other aquarium fishes, and for the common afflictions you should follow the directions for diagnosis and treatment in any good disease textbook. This section will deal with diseases caused by parasites found on wild cichlids, not as an aid to treatment, but simply for diagnostic purposes. With all the new cichlids being imported from previously inaccessible areas, it is likely that new parasites will turn up. It is hoped that aquarists will preserve these exotic parasites and send them either to me or to another parasitologist.

The only virus so far reported from cichlids is lymphocystis virus from the newly imported *Cichlasoma synspilum* of Guatemala. The virus produces strawberry-like boils on the surface of the fish in advanced cases. If this disease is suspected, the fish should be shipped *alive* to Dr. B. L. Middlebrooks, Department of Microbiology, University of Texas Medical Branch, Galveston, Texas. Preserved specimens are worthless, for Dr. Middlebrooks is engaged in maintaining live viruses in fish tissue culture for studies on their life cycles and structures.

The flagellated protozoan *Hexamita truttae* is known from the intestine of various fishes, and has been reported from *Pterophyllum scalare*. Intestinal smears or live fishes should be sent to the Eastern Fish Diseases Laboratory, Kearneysville, West Virginia. *Spironucleus elegans* is another flagellate from this same host, and the same directions should be followed as for *Hexamita*.

The Haemosporidea are another group of protozoa, and these are usually found in the blood. A blood smear is necessary for diagnosis, and perhaps your family physician or dentist will do this for you. *Babesiosoma (Dactylosoma) mariae* was reported from several species of *Haplochromis* from Lake Victoria. It may occur in other cichlids of East African lakes as well, but apparently has not been looked for.

The digenetic trematodes are a large group, and many species have been reported from cichlids. The following is a partial list of adult worms and their locations in various kinds of cichlids.

Parasite	Fish	Location
Allocreadium chuscoi	*Aequidens pulcher*	intestine
A. wallini	*Crenicichla geayi*	intestine
Crassicutis cichlasomae	*Cichlasoma mayorum*	stomach
Trematobrien haplochromios	*Haplochromis moffati*	intestine
Plagioporus biliaris	*Haplochromis flavii*, *Tilapia zillii*	gall bladder
Plagioporus sp.	*Tilapia* spp.	intestine

Discus fish with extensive destruction of tissue and secondary infections. Several kinds of parasites could cause the same symptoms and only microscopic examination could pin down the specific disease agent. Photo by H. Reichenbach-Klinke.

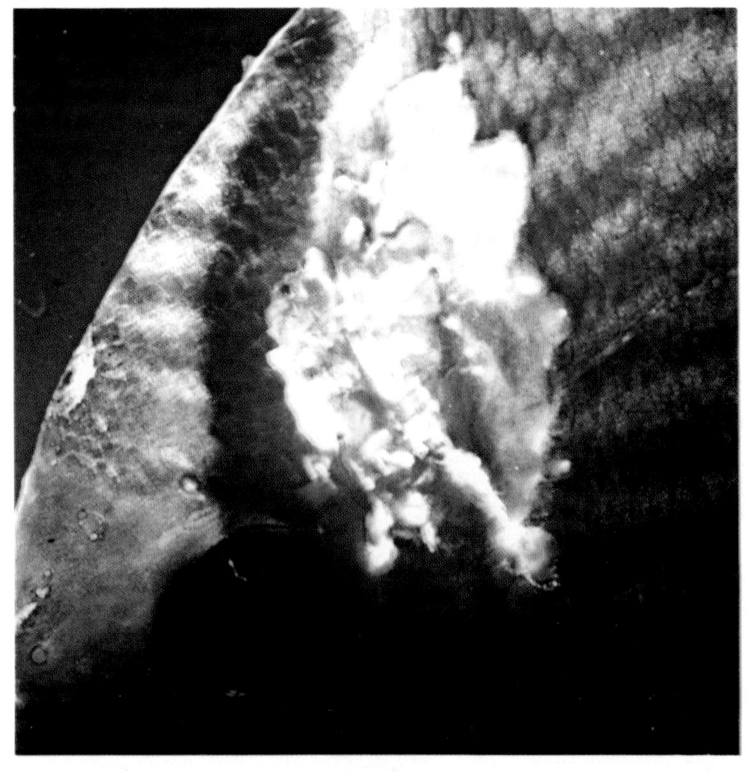

Metacercaria of *Clinostomum* (yellow grub trematode) in the eye of a pond-raised *Pelvicachromis pulcher*. Photo by Ruda Zukal.

Only a few larval forms are known from cichlids. These are usually metacercariae in the fish awaiting ingestion by a fish-eating bird, in which the parasite will attain maturity. *Haplorchis* sp. occurs in the skin and muscles of *Haplochromis flavii*; *Clonorchis sinensis* (an important parasite of man) occurs in the muscles of *Tilapia* species; and *Stictodora sclerogonocotyla* occurs in the muscles of *Tilapia galilaea*.

The presence of larval digenea is easily determined by observing either black spots or yellow lumps on the body or fins of the fish. The presence of internal (adult) digenea can be determined by finding eggs in the fecal samples of live fish, or recovering the worms from a killed fish. Generally, these worms are *not* a cause of fish death.

Monogenetic trematodes or flukes are typically external parasites of cichlids, but an unusual exception is known. External monogenea should be suspected if the fish undergo quite a bit of scratching and show inflamed patches on the body or expanded gill covers and rapid breathing. Treat with four drops of commercial formaldehyde solution to the gallon of tank water. The life cycle of monogenea is direct, and we don't have larval stages to worry about. However, one fish can directly infect other fishes, and for this reason it is not a bad idea to treat all imports, on arrival, with the formalin solution method.

Parasite	**Host**
Gyrodactylus cichlidarum	*Tilapia* spp., *Hemichromis fasciatus*, *"Hemichromis" bimaculatus*
Cichlidogyrus arthracanthus	*Tilapia zillii*
C. tiberianus	*T. zillii*
C. bychowskii	*Hemichromis fasciatus, "H." bimaculatus*
C. longicornis	*Tilapia* spp.
C. cirratus	*Tilapia galilaea*
C. nematocirrus	*T. nilotica*
C. tilapiae	*T. busumana, T. nilotica, T. galilaea*
C. lagoonaris	*T. melanotheron, T. guineensis*
C. dionchus	*T. galilaea, Chromidotilapia guentheri, Hemichromis fasciatus*
C. longicirrus	*Hemichromis fasciatus, Chromidotilapia guentheri*
C. halini	*Tilapia melanotheron, T. guineensis*
Gussevia spiralocirra	*Pterophyllum scalare*
Urocleidus cavanaughi	*Aequidens maroni*
U. aequidens	*A. maroni*
Enterogyrus cichlidarum (an internal species)	*Tilapia zillii, T. nilotica*
Onchobdella voltensis	*Hemichromis fasciatus, "H." bimaculatus, Chromidotilapia guentheri*
O. aframae	*Hemichromis fasciatus, Chromidotilapia guentheri*
O. spiricirra	*"Hemichromis" bimaculatus*
O. pterygialis	*"Hemichromis" bimaculatus*
O. krachii	*Chromidotilapia guentheri*

Tapeworms are not commonly reported from cichlids, and this is most likely due to a failure of persons to look for them. The few reports consist of *Proteocephalus bivitellatus* from *Tilapia* sp. in Sierra Leone; both *P. macrophallus* and *P. microscopius* from *Cichla ocellaris* in Brazil; and *Bothriocephalus musculosus* from *Aequidens portalegrensis* in an aquarium. Tapeworms are intestinal parasites and can sometimes be diagnosed by finding either the segments or eggs in feces. They are innocuous parasites and should not be purged, as the treatment is worse than the condition.

Roundworms can be serious pests of fishes, but they often occur in the tissues from which they cannot be removed. Intestinal worms might be removed by feeding dog or cat food containing thiabendazole (a general nematocide). The following nematodes (roundworms) have been reported from cichlids. *Capillaria*

Congenital deformity in young cichlids. Photo by Ruda Zukal.

pterophylli from *Pterophyllum scalare* in South America; *Gendria tilapiae* from *Tilapia galilaea* from Niger; and *Asymphylodora tincae* from *Haplochromis flavii* in Israel.

The thorny-headed worms (Acanthocephala) are a small group of serious parasites. Their eggs may be found in fecal samples, but they are virtually impossible to treat. The one report from cichlids is of *Pandosentis iracundus* in the gut of *Aequidens pulcher* and *Crenicichla geayi* in Venezuela.

Hole-in-the-head disease can attack many species of cichlids. Its cause remains unknown. Photo by Dr. H. Reichenbach-Klinke.

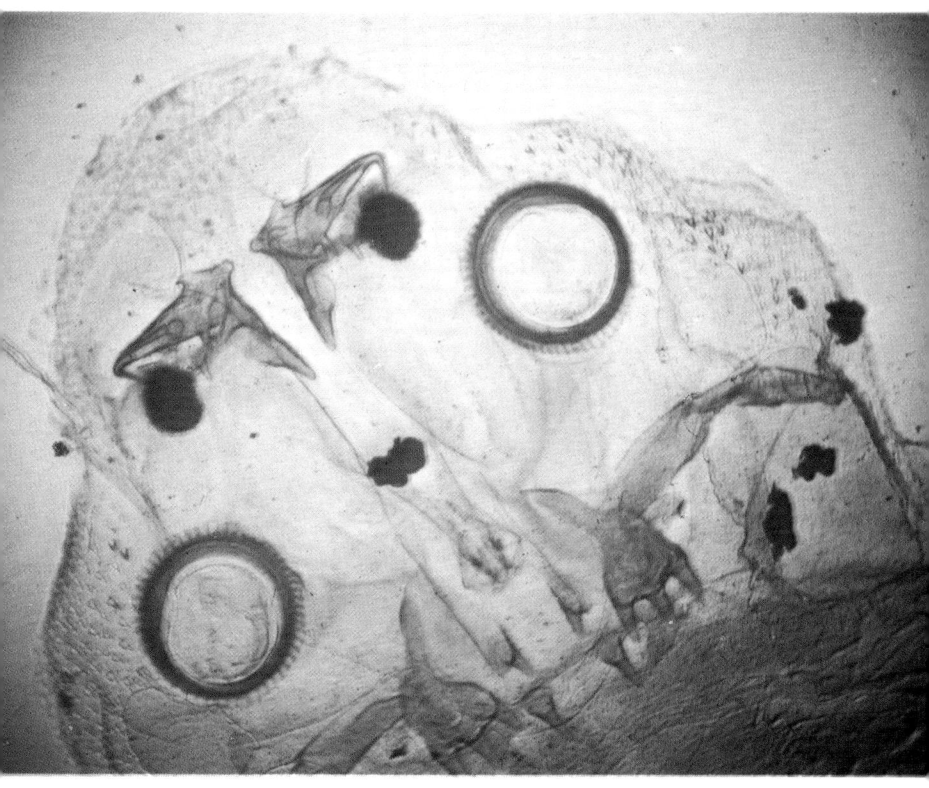

View of the common fish louse, *Argulus*, through the microscope. The circular areas are actually modified antennae that are now used for attachment. Photo by Dr. H. Reichenbach-Klinke.

Parasitic crustaceans are well-known from cichlids, and have been extensively studied in the East African lakes. There are a number of reports, and it would be best to divide them by taxonomic category.

Parasite	**Host**	**Locality**
BRANCHIURA		
Argulus cubensis	*Cichlasoma tetracanthus*	Cuba
A. exiguus	*Simochromis diagramma*	L. Tanganyika
A. africanus	*Tilapia* spp.	Africa
Dolops geayi	*Aequidens pulcher*	South America
D. geayi	*Crenicichla geayi*	South America

COPEPODA		
Ergasilus sarsi	*Tylochromis mylodon*	L. Tanganyika
E. kandti	*Tilapia P-congicus*	Africa
E. megacheir	*Tilapia P-congicus*	Africa
E. latus	*Tilapia* spp.	Africa
E. cunningtoni	*Tylochromis lateralis, Tilapia P-congicus, Tilapia* spp.	Africa
Paraergasilus lagoonaris	*Tilapia* spp.	Africa
Lernaea barnimiana	*Tilapia melanopleura*	Africa
L. palati	*Haplochromis chrysonotus, H. nkatae*	L. Malawi
L. tilapiae	*Tilapia* spp.	Africa
L. hardingi	*Sargochromis mellandi*	Africa
Opistholernaea laterobranchialis	*Tilapia macrochir*	Africa
Lamproglena monodi	Many cichlids	Africa
ISOPODA		
Lironeca tanganikae	*Simochromis diagramma*	L. Tanganyika
Artystone trysibia	*Symphysodon, Crenicichla, Geophagus*	South America

Members of the Branchiura are fish lice, easily seen on the surface of the host. Potassium permanganate, using the regimen given by Innes, is recommended. Among the Copepoda, *Ergasilus* and its allies are small parasites of the gills, recognizable by their enormous claspers. Potassium permanganate might be attempted, but there are no data on its effectiveness for this group of parasites. *Lernaea* and *Opistholernaea* are too difficult to treat. *Lamproglena* occurs on many lake cichlids and is found in the gills. I doubt whether it will respond to any of the usual treatments. Among the Isopoda, *Lironeca* is usually found in the mouth or under the gill plates, while *Artystone* is a huge creature that lives inside the body and eventually breaks through. All parasitic crustacea should be preserved and sent to a parasitologist. The isopods cannot be treated.

9

Cichlids of Asia

THE GENUS *ETROPLUS*

The genus *Etroplus* is discussed in Day's *Fishes of India, Ceylon and Burma.* This is the only genus of Asian cichlids and apparently is derived from a salt-tolerating primitive form which expanded into and along the coast of Africa, the Arabian Peninsula and southward along the west coast of India. Only three species are known: *E. maculatus*, *E. suratensis*, and *E. canarensis.*

The best-known *Etroplus* to the hobby is the orange chromide, *E. maculatus. E. suratensis* is called the green chromide, and is occasionally imported. *E. canarensis* is unknown to the hobby. All the species prefer some rock salt or marine salts in their water, but only *E. maculatus* may be easily maintained and even spawned in freshwater systems. The others probably are too dependent on brackish water for ready adaptability to aquaria.

The orange chromide has been intensively studied by behavioral biologists. See Barlow (1968, 1970), Ward and Barlow (1966), Quertermus and Ward (1969), and Cole and Ward (1969, 1970).

Orange chromides display intraspecific aggression when not spawning. Larger fish are likely to attack smaller ones. Barlow (1968) found that pair bond formation follows a peace treaty. (In humans, permanent pair bond formation, i.e., marriage, is often the signal for termination of a peace treaty!) One finds that pairs often consist of a larger male and smaller female. This appears related to the observation that males tend to attack females larger than they, whereas females tend to attack males smaller than themselves; further, pair bond formation seems to flow naturally out of aggression, via the peace treaty behavior. Result: the likelihood that the male will be larger than the female in a successful pairing. Barlow (1970) found similar results. He further showed that females had a tendency to form homosexual pairs or trios, but males did not have this tendency. Apparently females tend to evoke more courtship behavior than do males.

Ward and Barlow (1967) described breeding behavior of orange chromides. About a week after the pair bond has formed, spawning occurs on a rock or in a cave. The eggs hang from threads and both parents care for the brood, removing dead eggs and fanning the spawn. Pits are meanwhile dug in the gravel. Hatching occurs on the third day, and the wrigglers are moved to the pits for five or six days, after which they become free-swimming.

The fry shoal closely around either or both parents. During much of the time they glance off the sides of the adults. It was

Etroplus suratensis can be maintained in fresh water if the water is greatly hardened and some salt is added. This photograph illustrates an incorrect setup. Photo by Dr. Herbert R. Axelrod.

Etroplus suratensis, the green chromide. Photo by Dr. Herbert R. Axelrod.

Etroplus maculatus, the orange chromide. Photo by Ruda Zukal.

shown conclusively that during glancing the fry were feeding on the mucus secreted by the parent fishes. There are always a certain number of mucus cells in the skin of adult fishes, but the concentration of these cells during brooding increases by about a third. Parental slime is an important dietary component for the fry during the critical first week, and is of lesser importance thereafter. The fry can be raised apart from the parents, but keeping them with the parents usually yields much higher numbers of progeny raised.

In about three weeks or more protection terminates and the parents may prepare to spawn once again.

These authors also studied the coloration and patterns of adult fishes, but found little consistency. Some pairs become suffused with yellow when in nuptial condition, and this coloration increases to a peak at about the time the fry are ready to become free-swimming, one week after spawning. Orange chromides have a number of signals which their fry recognize. One of these is the danger signal, produced by flicking the rather dark pelvic fins. See Ward and Barlow (1967).

The chromides do best in alkaline and somewhat brackish water. A good set of conditions would include pH 7.5 to 8.5, some marine salts, and a temperature of 28°C (84°F). Imported chromides are not often seen, and the orange chromides in your local shop were probably produced in the ponds of fish farms in Florida.

Parvatheswararao (1967) studied wild *E. maculatus*. When the temperature was varied, he found variation in tissue water, cations and ascorbic acid. As the chromides probably invaded Asia along coastal waterways, their tolerance of high salt content is expected, and in this respect they resemble certain species of *Tilapia* and their allies, which are also coastal in fringe areas of their ranges.

As mentioned elsewhere in this book, *Etroplus* of Asia and the various cichlids of the island of Madagascar are closely related, and are generally closer to the ancestral cichlids than genera found on the mainlands of America and Africa.

10

New World cichlids

Despite the number and diversity of American cichlids, they nowhere nearly match the variation and abundance of cichlids of Africa. However, they are better known to American aquarists simply because of their long-time ready access to commercial dealers who brought them up from the Amazon, the Guianas, and other geographic areas with plane and boat facilities. And yet, despite years of familiarity to American aquarists (who supplied much of the information for their European colleagues), very many of these fishes were incorrectly identified as to species and region of origin. It has only been recently that much of the confusion was straightened out. Still, much more needs to be done to clarify the relationships and identities of, for example, the entire genus *Geophagus* and certain species groups within the huge genus *Cichlasoma*.

Ancestral American cichlids probably originated somewhere in South America, and their relatives in western Africa are part of the evidence that the two continents were at one time bridged. Africa and America are slowly drifting apart in the phenomenon known as continental drift, and one driving force is the continually buildingMid-Atlantic ridge, a gigantic submarine ridge line that is upwelling and moving the continents away from each other. (See also the **Introduction**).

The early American cichlids were not very different from *Aequidens* and *Chaetobranchus* on the one hand (both related to *Tilapia* of Africa) and *Cichla* (related to the African *Haplochromis*) on the other. The relationships of American cichlids will be further discussed below. But for now we might point out that the common South American genera include *Aequidens, Cichla, Crenicichla, Batrachops, Pterophyllum, Apistogramma, Nannacara, Astronotus* and *Geophagus*. There are many other minor genera closely related to one or the other of these.

Geophagus jurupari, juvenile. Photo by Dr. Herbert R. Axelrod.

The Rio Purus, Brazil. This large river arises in the Peruvian Andes and flows northeastward, emptying into the Amazon near Manaus. Photo by Harald Schultz.

A species of *Aequidens* from the Rio Branco. This river begins just over the border of Guyana and flows southward, where it joins the Rio Negro in Brazil. The Rio Negro meets the Amazon at Manaus. Photo by Dr. Herbert R. Axelrod.

Tributary of the Guarico River at Camatagua. This stream is part of the Orinoco River basin of Venezuela. Photo by Dr. Herbert R. Axelrod.

Cichlasoma, on the other hand, while found over large areas of South America, didn't really come into its evolutionary own until it began moving northward and invading Central America. It is in Central America that this genus and some of its derivatives have really undergone extensive speciation. The northward invasion extended to some of the islands of the Caribbean, while along the land mass the most northern point of invasion was Texas. Thus, cichlids occur in the two Americas and outlying islands. Why cichlids did not extend farther northward is probably based on a combination of factors, including mountain chains and the existence of sunfishes (family Centrarchidae), which failed to give way to these ecologically similar fishes from the south. We know from fishery introductions that temperature is not a sufficient blockade to cichlid invasion.

Most of the cichlids of the New World come from the tropical regions of South America.

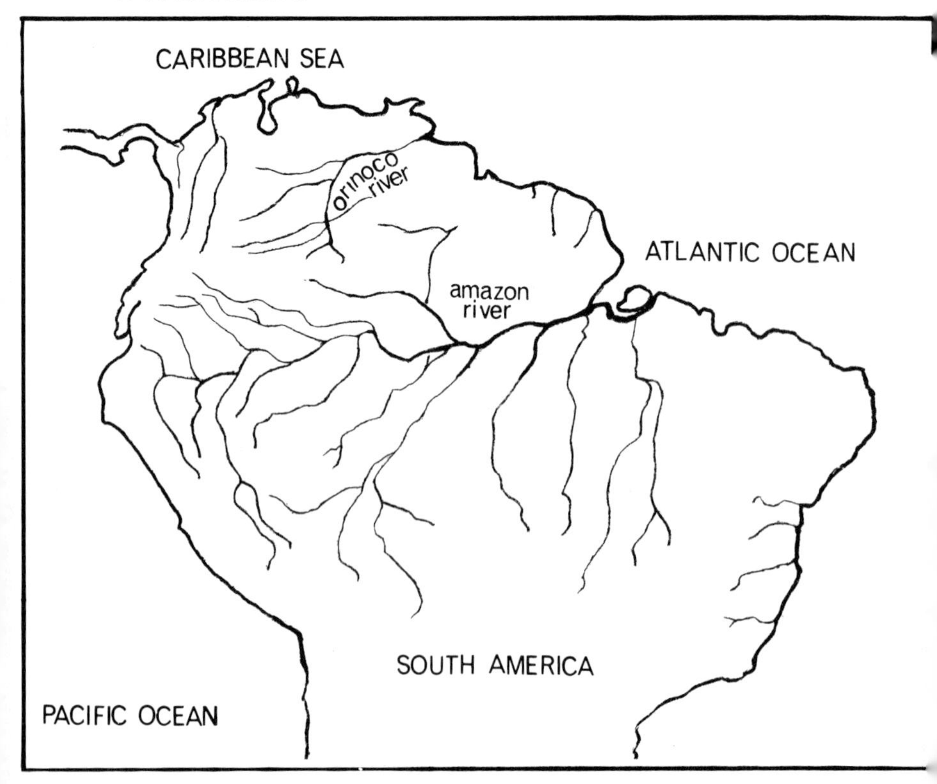

Most American cichlids are substratum spawners, preferring pits in muddy or sandy areas or hard substrata on which to spawn. A few, notably some species of *Geophagus* and the closely related *Biotodoma,* are mouthbrooders. In the aquarium cichlids will adapt to whatever is available. A pit spawner will go ahead and spawn on a bare bottom slate tank, and sand or gravel is not necessary to induce spawning. Many of the hard substratum spawners are also cave spawners, and will accept caves of rocks or flowerpots in the aquarium, or they may spawn on the glass itself. Some spawn on the leaves of large underwater plants, or the walls of caves. Aquarists interested in raising quantity usually remove the eggs from the parents and handle them using artificial incubation. This induces the parents to spawn much sooner than had they been allowed to raise their own families, and it is also recommended for skittish species.

Gery (1969) briefly reviewed the history and distribution of the freshwater fishes of South America. Though not as rich as Africa, the cichlid fauna nevertheless consists of about twenty genera with 100 to 150 species. According to Gery (1969: 828):—

> In the nineteenth century began a chain of great Brazilian expeditions with NATTERER, whose collections were studied by HAECKEL, KNER, and STEINDACHNER; VON SPIX and VON MARTIUS, whose collections, destroyed during the bombing of Munich, gave rise to the classical work of AGASSIZ; and above all Louis AGASSIZ himself in the famous THAYER Expedition (about 1865), shortly after joined and followed by Franz STEINDACHNER in the HASSLER Expedition. In the meantime, British Guiana and Rio Branco had been explored by the brothers Robert and Richard SCHOMBURGK (1835–1844), whose drawings and material were published, independently, by JARDINE, by VALENCIENNES (after CUVIER'S death) and by MULLER and TROSCHEL; whereas REINHARDT collected in the Rio São Francisco and published (as did LUTKEN) his discoveries in Copenhagen between 1849 and 1875. GUNTHER presented the first comprehensive survey of S.A. in his 'Catalogue' (completed 1870), thanks to different, but important, collections in the British Museum. EIGENMANN & EIGENMANN (1891) estimated the number of species to be more than 1,100.
>
> The first quarter of the twentieth century is marked by the meticulous reference work of Carl EIGENMANN, who explored systematically various parts of S.A. (British Guiana, Colombia, Chile), or worked on collections made by others: Paraguay by ANISITS, Amazon by J. HASEMAN (Carnegie Museum Expedition) and Rio Negro by TERNETZ (perhaps the largest ever made, not yet fully exploited). EIGENMANN'S work was continued by his

pupil G. S. MYERS and a number of the latter's own students, among whom one can cite some prominent contemporary U.S. ichthyologists like W. GOSLINE, J. BOEHLKE and S. WEITZMAN. Many others, American as well as European, also devoted part of their studies to neotropical fishes. They are too numerous to be cited, but it is impossible to ignore several works by H. W. FOWLER (Philadelphia), whose check-list of Brazil (1951–1954) is of daily use.

Myers (1964) sketched the history of ichthyology in America up to 1850, and this very readable paper is profusely illustrated with portraits of the giants in the field, including: Rafinesque, Mitchill, LeSueur, Holbrook, Günther, Boulenger, Regan, Norman, Agassiz, Steindachner, Garman, Carl Eigenmann, Baird, Gill, Goode, Bean, Cope, Meek, Fowler, Jordan, Evermann, Gilbert and several others.

Apistogramma sp., a dwarf cichlid of tropical America. Photo by H. J. Richter.

Aequidens pulchra, the blue acara. Known variously as *A. pulcher* and *A. latifrons*. Photo by Stanislav Frank.

RELATIONSHIPS AMONG AMERICAN CICHLIDS

Long ago, South America and Africa appear to have been connected. We can find similarities among *Tilapia* and its allies in Africa with most South American cichlids, in the structure of the pharyngeal hookup to the skull. What happened in the Americas? First of all, cichlid evolution proceeded throughout vast areas of South America and was not interfered with by northern fishes. Apparently there was an oceanic connection around Colombia and Panama, and this was an effective deterrent to southward migration (and competition) of northern fishes. A number of genera evolved in South America, based on the body plan of *Aequidens*. Typical South American derivatives of *Aequidens* are *Geophagus, Apistogramma, Nannacara, Acaronia* and *Astronotus*.

Later, in the late Pliocene or early Pleistocene, there was great geological activity resulting in the uplifting of the Andes Mountains, and as a result a land bridge was finally formed between North and South America. The entire Central American region was now available for invasion from the north and from the south, but the northern forms were already limited, largely by the mass of mountains and lakes to the north. And so, migration and invasion was primarily from south to north, with few exceptions. Much of this may be found reviewed in Myers (1966).

Aequidens itself didn't succeed very well in this new region, for only one species extends well into middle America (*Aequidens coeruleopunctatus*). But *Cichlasoma* did succeed, and a very recent speciation ensued. With *Cichlasoma* as the basic stock, derived from an *Aequidens*-like ancestor, it gave rise to the various "divisions" of *Cichlasoma* (see below), and to *Petenia, Herichthys, Herotilapia* and *Neetroplus* to the north. But *Cichlasoma* spread southward also, into *Aequidens* territory, and gave rise to *Uaru, Pterophyllum, Symphysodon* and other modern South American *Cichlasoma* species.

In a very important paper (Lowe-McConnell, 1969), the original relationships, as presented long ago by Regan in 1906, were summarized. In essence, a basic stock of ancestral cichlids gave rise on the one hand to *Cichla* and *Chaetobranchus,* and on the other hand to an Aequidens Group. The Aequidens Group, characterized by three anal spines, gave rise to several different evolutionary lines. One line led through *Crenicara* to the elongate *Batrachops* and *Crenicichla,* and this line was characterized by finely serrated preoperculars. Another line, characterized by lobes on the first gill arch, gave rise to *Geophagus* and *Apistogramma.* Three other distinct lines gave rise to *Nannacara, Acaronia* and *Astronotus.*

But this basic Aequidens Group was still not played out of possibilities. From this basic stock another group evolved, characterized by four or more anal spines, and this was the origin of *Cichlasoma.* In turn, the basic *Cichlasoma* stock gave rise to six other lines of evolution, leading to (1) *Petenia,* (2) *Pterophyllum* and *Symphysodon* (via a *C. severum*-like ancestor), (3) *Uaru,* (4) *Herotilapia,* (5) *Herichthys,* and (6) *Neetroplus.* Today *Herichthys* is considered a synonym of *Cichlasoma,* but that it may represent a distinct evolutionary line should not be overlooked.

THE GENUS *CICHLA*

The genus *Cichla* Bloch & Schneider, 1801 occupies a unique position among American cichlids in being the only genus which has a *Haplochromis* type of skull structure supporting the upper pharyngeal bones. In this arrangement, the upper pharyngeal bones are fused with the parasphenoid and basioccipital bones of the skull. (In the other type of arrangement, found in all other American cichlids, the parasphenoids alone contribute to the fusion; this is generally known as the *Tilapia* type of arrangement.)

Cichla contains at least two species, *C. ocellaris* Schneider, 1801 and *C. temensis* Humboldt, 1833. Both are cultivated in fish ponds in South America, and both are highly regarded game fishes, generally considered the Latin American equivalent of our large and smallmouth basses. *C. temensis* is rarely seen in the hobby, and was described by Lowe-McConnell (1969) as green, with

Young specimen of *Cichla ocellaris*. Photo by Harald Schultz.

All four photographs illustrate the same species, *Cichla ocellaris*. This large South American fish varies with age and geographic locality. It has been introduced into the waters of southern Florida as a game fish. Upper left photo by Harald Schultz, remaining three by Dr. Herbert R. Axelrod.

horizontal lines of light yellow spots. It is a more streamlined fish than *C. ocellaris,* with a more deeply notched caudal fin, shallower body, and more angular lower jaw. It is the largest South American cichlid known, attaining close to 30 inches in total length. *C. ocellaris,* while variable according to locality and water conditions, generally resembles our native yellow perch in having a deeper body, larger scales, several dark vertical bands which may be reduced to blotches, and brownish to olivaceous coloration with yellow or orange pigment in the lower fins.

Another nominal species, *C. chacoensis* Holmberg, 1891 was reported from Paraguay. Its validity is doubtful. I have no data on the validity of *C. orinocoensis,* but it appears to greatly resemble *C. ocellaris.*

Cichla species are predatory and attain large size. In nature, the fish breed in shallow water, digging a pit in hard mud, or several such pits. Colors intensify and males develop a hump on the back of the "neck". In *C. ocellaris,* the female's yellow breast now becomes orange. Spawns may number up to ten thousand eggs. Both parents guard the eggs and fry, but after about a month only the male guards the shoal, chasing the female away. In another month, the young are on their own. Recommended for ponds or exceptionally large aquaria.

THE GENUS *CHAETOBRANCHUS*

Chaetobranchus Heckel, 1840 is characterized by three anal spines and long, setiform (bristle-like) gill rakers. The type species, *C. flavescens* Heckel, 1840 is not known in the hobby. Invalid synonyms for *C. flavescens* include *C. robustus, Chromys ucayalensis* and *Geophagus badiipinnis.*

Another species, sometimes seen in the hobby, is *C. semifasciatus* Steindachner, 1875. It has an ocellus on the caudal fin, four broad bars on the upper part of the body, and thus differs from *C. flavescens* which lacks such markings. In the adult male there is a lateral blotch on the side, the caudal ocellus disappears, and the lower fins become solid red toward the outside, rather than red-striped (Lowe-McConnell, 1969). The fish is probably a plankton feeder, and the lack of a caudal ocellus in the adult led Lowe-McConnell to suggest that it might be a mouthbrooder.

Chaetobranchus semifasciatus. The body bars are mostly faded but can be seen. Photo by Harald Schultz.

(Substratum-brooders frequently display a caudal ocellus by which fry seem to orient to the parent.) The idea of plankton feeding is based on weak teeth, long, bristle-like gill rakers (a filtering apparatus?), and distribution in large, open bodies of water. Widely distributed in South America.

THE GENUS *CHAETOBRANCHOPSIS*

Species of *Chaetobranchopsis* Steindachner, 1875 superficially resemble those of the preceding genus, but differ in having more than three anal spines. They too have the long gill rakers and thus may be a genus of plankton feeders. Three species are known from South America: *C. australis* Eigenmann and Ward, 1907; the type species *C. orbicularis* (Steindachner, 1875) and *C. bitaeniatus* Ahl, 1936. The former is from Paraguay, and the two latter are from the Amazon drainage. *C. bitaeniatus* has been kept in the aquarium, but not bred. It is said to be peaceful, and not a digger.

Chaetobranchus bitaeniatus is now referred to as *Chaetobranchopsis bitaeniatus*. Photo by Dr. Herbert R. Axelrod.

Biotoecus opercularis, the only species currently recognized in the genus *Biotoecus*. Photo by Dr. Herbert R. Axelrod.

The use of parentheses around Steindachner's name may seem strange to readers, in that he apparently coined the genus name. The explanation is simple. Steindachner did coin the name, but considered it to be a subgenus within *Chaetobranchus*, based on what we now know to be superficial similarity. His subgenus was subsequently raised to generic rank, and that is why the year is the same, but Steindachner's name is in parentheses. Parentheses indicate that the species is now placed in a different genus from the one in which it was first placed.

DWARF AMERICAN CICHLIDS

A number of genera represent our dwarf American cichlids: *Apistogramma, Nannacara, Biotoecus, Crenicara* and some species of *Aequidens*. Thus, the dwarfs do not reflect a phylogenetically closely related group (but see below). From the basic Aequidens Group of ancestral cichlids, one line led to *Crenicara, Crenicichla*

Apistogramma wickleri, shown here, is very similar to *A. ortmanni*. Photo by Klaus Paysan.

Nannacara anomala, the goldeneye. The male of this pair is the upper fish. Photo by Ruda Zukal.

and *Batrachops*. Species of the latter two genera are by no means dwarf cichlids! Another line led to *Apistogramma* and *Geophagus* (and *Biotodoma*); only *Apistogramma* contains dwarf cichlids. A third line led to *Nannacara*. The origins of *Biotoecus* are not clear. *Aequidens* will not be treated as a "dwarf" genus, as only a few of its very many species would fall into this category. One conclusion appears warranted: all our dwarfs arose from the basic Aequidens Group of cichlids with three anal spines. The Cichlasoma Group, which is also an offshoot of the basic three anal spine group, did not give rise to any genera of dwarf cichlids.

THE GENUS *BIOTOECUS*

Biotoecus Eigenmann and Kennedy, 1903 contains the single species *B. opercularis* (Steindachner, 1894). The fish was originally placed in the now defunct genus *Saraca* Steindachner, 1875. This rare species (in the hobby) is Amazonian in distribution, originally reported from Lake Saraca in Brazil. In its subtly translucent greens and iridescent blues it resembles the young of our native sunfishes, but almost nothing is known of it as an aquarium fish. A derivative of the Aequidens Group. The change in generic name was necessary because *Saraca* had previously been used for a lepidopterous insect (butterflies and moths), and was thus unavailable. According to the Rules of Zoological Nomenclature, two unrelated natural groups of animals may not share the same generic name.

Biotoecus differs from the closely related *Apistogramma* and *Geophagus* in having a dorsal fin with VII-VIII/13-14 rays. The lateral line is very reduced. Anal fin rays III/7. Scales 29-30.

THE GENUS *NANNACARA*

The genus *Nannacara* Regan contains three species; *N. anomala* Regan, 1905, *N. taenia* Regan, 1912, and *N. bimaculata* Eigenmann, 1912. *N. taenia* is rare in the hobby (frequently absent), native to the Amazon, and very similar to *Aequidens curviceps;* in fact, one well-known aquarist believes all photos of "*taenia*" in the hobby actually are of *curviceps*. The golden eye dwarf cichlid, *N. anomala,* is very common and well-known, and native to northern

Nannacara anomala, male. Photo by Chvojka Milan.

Nannacara anomala, the goldeneye dwarf cichlid. The female has adopted the checkerboard brooding pattern, while the male's flanks are iridescent green. These photos, taken by Ruda Zukal, show the actual spawning. After spawning, the male will be driven off.

Aequidens curviceps has long been confused in the hobby literature with *Nannacara taenia*. Photo of *A. curviceps* by Harald Schultz.

South America. Very similar in appearance is *N. bimaculata,* which is distinguished from *N. anomala* by the presence of lateral and caudal spots.

A characteristic of the genus is the densely scaled head. The first gill arch does not have a downward projecting lobe. The upper (forward) lateral line runs very close to the base of the dorsal fin, and its overall appearance is to run obliquely upward toward the spiny part of the dorsal, but remain separated from that fin by no more than a single scale row. The lack of a lobe on the gill arch separates *Nannacara* from *Apistogramma,* and the closeness of the lateral line to the dorsal fin separates it from *Aequidens;* these are the only two genera with which *Nannacara* might be confused. The meristic counts are insufficient for separating the species, and photos or other visual descriptions are required. Relevant papers on *N. anomala* are Kuenzer (1962, 1964, 1965) and Goldstein (1967). See Kuenzer for quantitative data on ethological (behavioral) studies, and Goldstein for aquarium observations.

N. anomala, the goldeneye or slate or gray dwarf cichlid, is sexually dimorphic and dichromatic. Males are much larger in potential aquarium size (up to three inches or more) while females tend to remain well under two inches. The male develops streamers from the terminal soft rays of the dorsal and anal fin. In coloration the male tends to a grayish blue or grayish green color with considerable iridescence when in nuptial condition. The female (and young males, as well as males not in condition), is characterized by a dirty white or tan color to the body, with a horizontal dark band on each side. In nuptial condition, most marked immediately subsequent to spawning, she develops a pattern of horizontal and vertical bands resembling a checkerboard, plus a very dark face.

Goldeneyes will spawn readily and are good fish for the beginner. Tanks may be as small as five-gallon size for a pair, but somewhat larger and with additional fishes (of the same or related species) work just as well. In nuptial condition the male develops intense coloration and may be somewhat belligerent toward the female. Spawning usually occurs in some kind of rock or flowerpot cave, but may also occur out in the open or on the glass. Typically a hard substratum is chosen and not a gravel pit. Upon completion of spawning the female develops into a tiger and will drive the male and all other fishes as far from the clutch as she herself dares venture. She is an excellent parent and will protect eggs and fry to the best of her ability. As spawning may occur in a community tank in the recesses of a cave, the best indicator of the event is the appearance of the checkerboard pattern. If there is danger of the fry being picked off by the other tank inhabitants, you have the choice of removing all other fishes or removing the eggs for artificial incubation. Eggs hatch in two or three days at room temperature and the fry become free-swimming in a tight shoal in another five days. Start feeding at this time with newly hatched brine shrimp, or microworms if brine shrimp are not available. Growth is moderately fast and enhanced by frequent feedings and water changes. The average spawn consists of about a hundred eggs of which thirty fry will probably be raised.

Nannacara is a common fish in shipments from importers to pet shops, where they often come in as mixed dwarf cichlids together with several kinds of *Apistogramma*. Recently they have been coming in with a fish called the blue cichlid, which is just another *Apistogramma* of uncertain identity. In the past five years many of the shipments arriving at American pet stores have had rich flushes of orange coloration to the fins. This fish may be *N. bimaculata,* which has been described by Lowe-McConnell as similar to *N. anomala* but distinguished by lateral and caudal spots. Making eyeball identifications of cichlids on such tenuous characters as bands vs. spots is always a risky business, but I will go out on a limb this time, particularly as the original description of *N. anomala* makes no mention of spots on the flanks, but only of the stripes.

N. anomala has been known to guard and herd fry of other cichlids, including various species of *Apistogramma* and *Pelvicachromis pulcher*. This behavior is seen often among juvenile females. *N. taenia* has been reported in the hobby, but I have never seen this species and many reports referring to that name may in fact be based on observations of *Aequidens curviceps.*

Apistogramma ramirezi, pair. This fish will probably be placed in a different genus in the future. Photo by Timmerman.

THE GENERA *APISTOGRAMMA, APISTOGRAMMOIDES* AND *TAENIACARA*

Apistogrammoides contains the single species *A. pucallpaensis* Meinken, 1965 and little is known of its habits or requirements.

Taeniacara contains the single species *T. candidi* Myers, 1935. It greatly resembles *Apistogramma* in superficial characters, but differs in the structure of the first gill arch. (*Apistogramma weisei* Ahl, 1936 may be a junior synonym, but that has not yet been settled). In *T. candidi* there is no downward-projecting lobe on the first gill arch (there is no lobe there at all!), and in lacking this character, it is separable from the *Apistogramma-Apistogrammoides-Biotodoma-Geophagus* line of evolution.

Apistogramma is a tremendous group of difficult-to-identify species, ranging through most of South America. Dr. George S. Myers (personal communication) has seen approximately fifty

Apistogramma agassizi, male. This fish was named for the great American naturalist Agassiz. Photo by Timmerman.

The fish in this photograph has been identified as a female *Apistogramma amoenum*. However, it is extremely difficult to identify species of *Apistogramma* from photos of females, most of which are almost inseparable. Photo by H. J. Richter.

This fish, long thought to be *A. pertense,* is now known to be neither *pertense* nor *ornatipinnis*. Its code name is "Canoga Park," according to Drs. John Parsons and Harriette Schapiro of the *Apistogramma* Study Group of the American Cichlid Association. Photo by Dr. Herbert R. Axelrod.

distinct species of this genus, yet only a small number have been described and named to date. Some are pit spawners (e.g., *A. ramirezi*), but most are hard surface spawners (and *A. ramirezi* may choose this route on occasion). See the table for some data.

It is hopeless for the aquarist to attempt identifications merely on meristic counts. To avoid possible hybridization these fishes should be line bred, and pickled specimens ought to be sent to the United States National Museum (Natural History Museum). The aquarist is limited to making guesses based on excellent (not merely good) photographs. Egg colors are not good criteria either.

NOMINAL SPECIES OF *APISTOGRAMMA* REGAN

Name	Dorsal	Anal	Pectoral	Lateral scales
A. aequipinnis	XV/5	III/6	—	22
A. agassizi	XV–XVI/7	III/4–6	14	23
A. amblopIitoides	XIII/10	III/9	13	—
*A. amoenum**	XV/7	III/6	—	25
A. borellii	XVI/5–6	III/6–7	—	22–24
A. cacatuoides	XV/4–5	III/7	—	24–27
A. commbrae	XVI/5–6	III/6–7	11	22
A. gibbiceps	XIV–XVI/6–7	III/6–7	12–13	17–24
A. hoignei	XVI/7	III/6	12	23–24
A. klauswitzi	XVI/6–7	III/6	13	23–24
A. kleei	XVI/6	III/6	12–13	25–26
A. ornatipinnis	XV/7–8	III/6	—	21–24
A. ortmanni	XV/7	III/6–7	12	22–24
A. parva	XV/6	III/6	—	24
A. pertense	XVI/6	III/6	12–13	23
A. pleurotaenia†	XVI/6	IV(?)/5	—	23
A. ramirezi	XIV/XV/9	III/8	11–12	26–29
A. reitzigi	XVI/5	III/5	—	21
A. ritense	XV/6	III/6	—	21
A. rondoni	XV/6	III/6	—	22
A. steindachneri	XV/7	III/6	—	24
A. sweglesi	XV/7	III/6	11	24
A. taeniatum	XIV–XVI/6–7	III/6–7	—	23
A. trifasciatum	XV–XVI/6	III/5–6	—	22–27
A. weisei‡	XVI/6	III/4	—	22
A. wickleri	XV/7	III/7	11	23

* Haseman considered (1911) *amoenum* a junior synonym of *A. taeniatum*.
† Haseman (1911) considered this a junior synonym of *Heterogramma borellii*.
‡ *A. weisei* may be a junior synonym of *Taeniacara candidi*.

Hermann Meinken supplied me with an updated key to the species groups within *Apistogramma*. Notice that the important criteria include the snout length, caudal fin shape, and presence or absence of elongated dorsal fin rays.

KEY TO THE GENUS *APISTOGRAMMA*

1. Snout length of male and female greater than diameter of the eye—
   - A. Caudal of male rounded . . .no species known.
   - B. Caudal of male with elongated fin rays above and below (lyretail pattern).
     - *ortmanni* (Eig., 1912)—Brit. Guiana, Amaz.
     - *wickleri* Meink., 1960—Guiana?
2. Snout length of male and female equal to eye diameter—
   - A. Caudal of male rounded; forward dorsal spines not elongated.
     - *amblopltoides* Fowler, 1939—Peruv. Amazon
     - *hoignei* Meink., 1965—Venezuela
     - *steindachneri* ?(Regan, 1908)—Demerara(?)
   - B. Caudal of male with elongated rays above and below; fifth to eighth dorsal spines elongated.
     - *cacatuoides* Hoed., 1951—Dutch Guiana
     - *klauswitzi* Meink., 1962—middle Amazon
     - *kleei* Meink., 1964—Amazon?
     - *ornatipinnis* Ahl, 1936—Brit. Guiana
     - *sweglesi* Meink., 1961—Peruvian Amazon
     - *t. trifasciatum* (Eig. and Kenn., 1903)—Par.
     - *t. haraldschultzi* Meink., 1961—Matto Grosso
     - *t. maciliense* (Haseman, 1911)—mid. Amazon
3. Snout length of male and female less than diameter of the eye—
   - A. Caudal of male rounded.
     - (a) forward dorsal spines not elongated.
       - *aequipinnis* Ahl, 1938—La Plata basin?
       - *amoenus* (Cope, 1872)—Ambyiacu and La Plata
       - *commbrae (=corumbae?)* (Reg., 1906)—Mat. Gros.
       - *pertense* (Haseman, 1911)—mid. Amaz., Tapajoz
       - *pleurotaenia* (Reg., 1909)—La Plata, Par., Braz.
       - *reitzigi* Ahl, 1939—Paraguay
     - (b) fifth to eighth dorsal spines elongated.
       - *ramirezi* Myers and Harry, 1948—Rio Meta
       - *parva* Ahl, 1931—lower Amazon, Paraguay
       - *taeniatum* (Günther, 1862)—Parag. Amazon
   - B. Caudal of male with elongated rays above and below; fifth to eighth dorsal spines elongated.
     - *borellii* (Regan, 1906)—Paraná, Matto Grosso
     - *rondoni* Miranda-Ribeiro, 1918—Matto Grosso
     - *ritense?* (Haseman, 1911)—Paraná, Paraguay
   - C. Caudal of male with central rays elongated.
     - (a) no elongated dorsal rays.
       - *agassizi* (Steind., 1875)—Amazon, Paraná to Paraguay
       - *gibbiceps* Meink., 1969—Rio Negro
     - (b) fifth to eighth dorsal spines elongated.
       - *weisei* Ahl, 1935—middle Amazon

RELATED SPECIES: *Apistogrammoides pucallpaensis* Meinken, 1965.

The markings in the caudal fin of this species place it in the *A. cacatuoides* complex of species.

Apistogramma amblopIitoides. Photo by Harald Schultz.

This fish, long thought to be *Apistogramma borelli*, is now considered to be either *A. cacatuoides* or a closely related species. Male above and female below. Photos by H. J. Richter.

Notice that some of the species names listed in the table do not appear in Meinken's key; this probably reflects his feelings that some names are likely synonyms of others. A problem exists with respect to the identification of a species characterized by a series of wavy lines in its lower half. This fish has previously been regarded by aquarists as *A. borellii*. However, in his original description of *Heterogramma borellii* Regan (1906) made no mention of such wavy lines, nor did Haseman (1911) some years later. In his same paper, Regan (1906) described *A. commbrae* (note the correct spelling) in part as: ". . . each series of scales of the lower part of the body with a more or less distinct dark longitudinal stripe . . ."; but in other respects this description does not fit our wavy-lined fish. It should also be noted that the fish with the wavy lines is quite similar in practically all color and pattern characters with *A. cacatuoides*. Thus, the use of the name *borellii* for our wavy-lined *Apistogramma* is probably erroneous, the fish probably being *cacatuoides* or a related species. The relationship between *commbrae* and *cacatuoides* is an open question, pending further information, although Meinken feels there are adequate differences between them.

Lobe on first (outer) gill arch of *Apistogramma agassizi*. Photo by Dr. R. J. Goldstein.

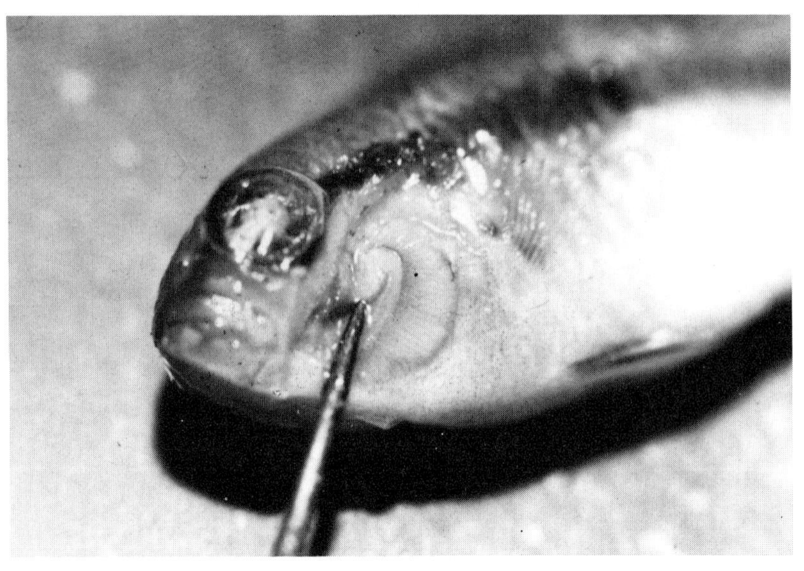

An unidentified species of *Apistogramma*. Photo by Harald Schultz.

Apistogramma agassizi, male. Photo by Chvojka Milan.

Apistogramma ornatipinnis, hopefully! This fish was previously thought to be *commbrae*, but *commbrae* has a rounded caudal fin. Photo by Arend van den Nieuwenhuizen.

Apistogramma kleei, illustrated here, lacks the wavy lines of *A. cacatuoides* and the clean dark horizontal bands of *A. trifasciatum*. It is now commonly available in the hobby. Photo by Karl Knaack.

Apistogramma klausewitzi, named for the well-known German ichthyologist, Dr. Wolfgang Klausewitz. Photo by Harald Schultz.

A member of the *Apistogramma ortmanni—A. ornatipinnis* species complex. Photo by Dr. Herbert R. Axelrod.

Species of *Apistogramma* have undergone a good deal of nomenclatural shifting about, a number of them originally placed as subspecies within other species, and subsequently elevated to full species rank by various authors. An old name for the group, no longer used, is *Heterogramma*. Klee (1971) has presented compelling arguments to place *A. ramirezi* in the genus *Geophagus*, and pointed out that the name *Microgeophagus* has no validity whatever. Because of the difficulty inherent in defining the nominal species of *Geophagus*, I prefer to leave *A. ramirezi* within *Apistogramma* for the present, especially as the genus *Geophagus* is now being carefully studied. It is likely that in a few years the genus *Geophagus* will be unscrambled and the special problem of *A. ramirezi* will be resolved.

Most species of *Apistogramma* and their allies require clean water, warmth, and privacy. They seem to do well as pairs in seven-to ten-gallon aquaria with sand or gravel, a flowerpot or rocky region with caves, rooted and floating plants, filtration, and good incandescent light. Living foods should constitute most of the diet, supplemented with a good flake food in the absence of a variety of living foods. I recommend live brine shrimp, *Tubifex*,

Apistogramma ornatipinnis. Photo by Timmerman.

Apistogramma trifasciatum haraldschultzi. Presently considered only a subspecies, this form may deserve full species rank. Photo by Dr. Herbert R. Axelrod.

bloodworms, *Daphnia,* and mosquito larvae, or at least a combination of two of these. Some species breed better when maintained as communities in larger tanks, and *A. ramirezi* is a good example.

Many of the species are switch spawners, breeding either on a hard surface or in a pit. The tendency, however, is for *A. ramirezi* to spawn in pits, and most of the others to choose hard surfaces, including plant leaves, rocks, and the aquarium glass. Most of these fishes are not the best of parents, and artificial incubation of the eggs is advised for at least the first couple of spawns (until you have all the fry you want). If you are breeding them in a large community, the fry have a better chance of being cared for than if you are breeding them in a one-pair tank.

Apistogramma ramirezi tending its eggs. Photo by H. J. Richter.

Apistogramma reitzigi. Photo by Wolfgang Bechtle.

Apistogramma trifasciatum. Photo by Hilmar Hansen.

Collecting fishes in South America. Dwarf cichlids are often found in soft, acid water in nature, with many decaying plants. Many aquarists try to duplicate such set-ups in home aquaria, with rather foreseeable results. Photo by Harald Schultz.

It is all right to mix a species of *Apistogramma* with one of *Nannacara,* but avoid keeping similar species of *Apistogramma* in the same aquarium unless you are absolutely certain that you can tell the females apart. A large community of one species in a well-lit, clean and prettily planted aquarium is a pleasing sight. However, it is important to rapidly remove damaged or beaten fish, and maintain the water at its peak of cleanliness with water changes, siphoning, and water sprite at the surface. These fishes all succumb to infections by bacterial pathogens in dirty tanks, and laxity in management will not be tolerated.

The wild type *A. ramirezi* is a lovely blue fish. A number of golden strains are available, of varying quality, but these sports are still just domestic varieties (and not subspecies) of *Apistogramma ramirezi.* Thus, "ram" and "golden ram" are the names generally applied to the strains.

There is always a demand by the hobby magazines for excellent color slides of species of *Apistogramma,* and the aquarist-photographer should take advantage of this source of pocket money.

THE GENUS *ACARONIA*

The genus *Acaronia* Myers, 1940 contains *A. nassa* and *A. trimaculata*. An earlier name for this genus of fishes was *Acaropsis*, but that name was illegally used because it already belonged to another genus of the animal kingdom. Myers then chose *Acaronia* as a replacement name.

Very similar to *Aequidens*, but with a large mouth, protractile premaxillaries, and the end of the maxilla exposed when the mouth is closed. Omnivorous, sometimes predaceous fishes of solitary habits. No breeding information available. *Acaronia* is a derivative of the Aequidens Group of ancestral cichlids. Another nominal species, *A. rondoni*, is now considered a member of *Apistogramma* by Meinken, but was placed in *Acaronia* by Fowler (1954).

THE GENUS *CRENICARA*

Crenicara Steindachner, 1875 is a dwarf cichlid genus closely related to the pike cichlids of the genera *Crenicichla* and *Batrachops*. In fact, these three genera form a natural group which arose from the primitive Aequidens Group. All three genera share serrated (saw-toothed) edged preoperculars. In *Crenicara* the scales of the lateral line are the same size as the scales above and below. But in the other two genera, the lateral line scales are different in size from the surrounding scales.

In *Crenicara* the mouth is small and the total size is small. With the equality of lateral line and surrounding scales, plus the serrated preopercular edges, it is easy to see that this genus is very distinct and unlikely to be confused by ichthyologists with anything else. Unfortunately aquarists cannot say the same for the disposition of species.

Species of *Crenicara* are not infrequent imports from the Guyanas and Amazon, but the delineation of species by aquarists is usually based on past aquarium literature, which indicates only two species: *C. maculata* and *C. filamentosa*, and which are quite different. A reading of the major ichthyological literature supplies a different view.

The type of the genus is *C. punctulata* (Günther, 1863). Both Regan (1905) and Lowe-McConnell (1969) describe this species as

Acaronia nassa, showing the young fish above and the more mature ones below. Upper photo by Harald Schultz; lower photo by Dr. Herbert R. Axelrod.

Crenicara filamentosa, male above. Photo by Dr. Edward Schmidt.

Crenicara maculata, female. Photo by Klaus Paysan.

brownish in preservative, with a series of dark blotches above the lateral line and a more distinct series below it. A dark stripe with white edges runs the length of the fish's eye to its mouth; a dark stripe runs from the operculum to the end of the caudal fin. From the middle of the dorsal rearward, and on the middle of the caudal, occur light and dark stripes or spots. The anal fin has a blackish edge. The caudal fin is said to be rounded.

Another species, better known to aquarists, is *C. maculata* (Steindachner, 1875) originally placed in the presently invalid genus *Dicrossus*. According to Regan (1905), this fish is marked the same as *C. punctulata*! Furthermore, its caudal is also said to be rounded.

Rather different from the preceding species is *C. altispinosa* Haseman, 1911. According to the original description, there are dark bands beneath the eyes, continuing above the eyes and meeting halfway between the eyes and dorsal fin origin. Operculum dark. The fins are usually colorless, but the membranes of the first five dorsal spines are sometimes dark. Six dark lateral bands

Crenicara filamentosa, male. Photo by Paul V. Loiselle.

extend from the dorsal to the lower flank. In some fishes other characteristics are sometimes seen, including brown lines associated with the scale rows, dark edged anal and caudal fins, and white bands or lines from the eyes to the snout. The fish is deep bodied, in contrast to the elongate other species of the genus.

Crenicara filamentosa is known to the hobby as a dark, lyretail type of dwarf cichlid. I have seen very good specimens, alive, on occasion. It seems to be a distinct species, but the original description is quite brief. Occasional specimens of *C. filamentosa* are found in shipments of imported cardinal tetras. This cichlid is brownish in basic body coloration, whereas *C. maculata* is dirty white, with some red coloration to the fins.

Recently, some of the fish farms in Florida have offered a fish for sale under the name *C. maculata.* This identification seems to be entirely correct, but some confusion has resulted from the fact that males tend to have lyre-like extensions on the caudal fin, in addition to very rich coloration. The confusion is easily resolved, however, by noting that few specimens of *Crenicara* have been studied by ichthyologists, the fishes seeming to be uncommon in nature. Pictures in the previous aquarium literature have been of either juveniles or females. *C. maculata* has fourteen dorsal spines, whereas the similarly marked *C. punctulata* has sixteen or seventeen. Neither *C. filamentosa* nor *C. altispinosa* should be confused with anything else.

C. filamentosa and *C. maculata* are very peaceful cave-spawners, and should be kept under similar conditions as given to species of *Apistogramma.* The other species are unknown to the hobby.

THE GENUS *BATRACHOPS*

Batrachops Heckel, 1840 is a genus of pike cichlids distinguished from *Crenicichla* in two easily discernible ways: the teeth of *Batrachops* are all non-depressible, and the dorsal spines generally range from 18 to 24; in *Crenicichla* some of the teeth are depressible and there are generally fewer dorsal spines.

Batrachops is roughly defined as elongate, with moderate ctenoid scales; scales of the lateral line larger than the rest; mouth moderate to large; lower jaw projecting; teeth conical, in two or three series in each jaw, the outermost series enlarged (especially

Crenicichla dorsiocellata. In the fish above the dorsal spot is well defined; in the fish below the spot has become obscure. Photos by Harald Schultz.

Crenicichla lepidota grows to a length of about 8 inches. Photo by Harald Schultz.

Crenicichla lenticulata. Photo by Harald Schultz.

in the lower jaw); none of the teeth depressible. There are several other characters as well. The scale counts have been given in different ways by different authors, some indicating scales above and those below the lateral line, and some indicating total scale rows including those before and after the ends of the lateral line. Thus, I have chosen to omit these data from the list of species with their dorsal and anal counts.

No species of *Batrachops* is known with certainty to have been established as an aquarium fish. Some of the unidentified pike cichlids in the hobby may belong within this genus. All species are South American in distribution, and all are predaceous.

SPECIES OF *BATRACHOPS* HECKEL, 1840

	Dorsal rays	Anal rays
B. cyanotus (Cope, 1871)	XXIV/11	III/8
B. nemopterus Fowler, 1939	XVIII/12	III/8
B. ocellatus (Perugia, 1897)	XXII/11	III/8
B. punctulatus Regan, 1905	XXIII–XXIV/11–13	III/7–8
B. reticulatus Heckel, 1840	XXII–XXIV/11–12	III/8
B. scottii Eigenmann, 1907	—	—
B. semifasciatus Heckel, 1840	XXII–XXIII/10–12	III/7–10

An unknown species of *Crenicichla*, probably *C. lepidota*. Photo by G. Marcuse.

This slender fish has been dubbed *Crenicichla saxatilis*. Photo by G. Marcuse.

THE GENUS *CRENICICHLA*

Crenicichla Heckel, 1840 contains a large group of fishes known as pike cichlids in the hobby. The genus is similar to *Batrachops* (which are also called pike cichlids), but differs in a few ways. The genus may be roughly defined as: elongate fishes, predaceous, usually with large mouths; margin of preoperculum usually serrate; lower jaw projecting; teeth of inner series depressible; scales of lateral line larger than those above or below it; scales ctenoid or cycloid; South American in distribution. Juveniles and adults often differently marked.

The genus is large and complex. Both the upper and lower lateral line are quite long, and the scales of the lateral lines have been counted in various ways. Lowe-McConnell uses the scales above the lateral line as taxonomic characters, but as her concern was with only a small number of species of this genus, I have not chosen to present the scale counts. The size of the genus, as indicated in the table of species, ought to suffice to indicate that these fishes are extremely difficult to identify with any certainty, except for a very few species.

The species of *Crenicichla* are all very similar. This one is *C. wallacei*. Photo by Harald Schultz.

Crenicichla macrophthalma. This specimen was collected in Camatagua, Venezuela in 1971. Photo by Dr. Herbert R. Axelrod.

Crenicichla geayi. The half-banded pike cichlid comes from the Central Amazon region. Photo by Harald Schultz.

Species of *Crenicichla* are substratum breeders. See Longfellow (1970) for a detailed report on breeding *C. lepidota.* Pike cichlids will occasionally spawn in aquaria, in flower pot caves. Once a pair has spawned, it will likely spawn regularly thereafter. Spawns are large, as expected in so large a fish (about five to ten inches in aquaria). Recommended only for the devoted cichlidophile with plenty of tank space. They will get along with other large fishes in a community tank without much difficulty. Live foods preferred.

SOME NOMINAL SPECIES OF *CRENICICHLA* HECKEL, 1840

	Dorsal rays	Anal rays
C. acutirostris Günther, 1862	XXIV/14	III/11
C. cametana Steindachner, 1911	—	—
C. cincta Regan, 1905	XXII–XXIII/15	III/12
C. iguassuensis Haseman, 1911	XX–XXII/11	III/8–9
C. jaguarensis Haseman, 1911	XIX/11	III/8
C. lacustris (Castelnau, 1855)	XX–XXIII/12–13	III/8–10
C. marmorata Pellegrin, 1903	—	—
C. santaremensis Haseman, 1911	XXI/11	III/6–7
C. simoni Haseman, 1911	XXII/11	III/7
C. ternetzi Norman, 1926	—	—
C. brasiliensis (Bloch)	—	—
C. anthurus Cope, 1872	XXII/10	III/8
C. dorsocellata Haseman, 1911	XX–XXIII/10–13	III/8
C. lepidota Heckel, 1840	XVII–XVIII/13–14	III/8–10
C. saxatilis (Linnaeus, 1758)	XVII–XX/13–16	III/8–10
C. johanna Heckel, 1840	XXI–XXIV/16–17	III/11–12
C. alta Eigenmann, 1912	XVIII–XIX/13–15	III/9–10
C. geayi Pellegrin, 1903	XXII/11	III/8–9
C. wallacii Regan, 1905	XX–XXI/9–11	III/7–9
C. macrophthalma Heckel, 1840	XX–XXII/10–13	III/7–9
C. lugubris Heckel, 1840	XXII–XXIII/15–17	III/10–12
C. lucius Cope, 1871	XIX–XXI/13–14	III/10
C. vittata Heckel, 1840	XXIII/13–14	III/9–10
C. multispinosa Pellegrin, 1903	XXIV–XXV/13–14	III/9–10
C. nana Regan, 1913	—	—
C. lenticulata Heckel, 1840	XXI–XXII/17–18	III/12
C. ornata Regan, 1905	XXII/XXIII/17–19	III/11–12
C. strigata Günther, 1862	XXII/XXIII/17	III/11
C. notophthalma Regan, 1913	—	—
C. jupiaensis Britski & Luengo, 1968	—	—

THE GENUS *GEOPHAGUS*

The genus *Geophagus* Heckel, 1840 is closely related to *Apistogramma,* both genera derived from the three anal spine Aequidens Group ancestor, and both sharing a downward projecting lobe on the first gill arch, carrying marginal gill rakers which are short and in only moderate numbers. There is no notch between the spiny and soft portions of the dorsal fin, the teeth are conical, and the preoperculum is entire. *Geophagus* is separated from *Apistogramma* by only a few characters. First, the upper lateral line is usually separated from the dorsal by at least $2\frac{1}{2}$ scale rows; the lateral line bifurcates at the caudal peduncle; and the preorbital space (the distance from the mouth at the very front to the forward rim of the eye) may be as much as twice the eye diameter, giving these fishes a long-nosed look. The major paper on the taxonomy of the genus is Regan (1906). Other pertinent papers abound, and I have also used Haseman (1911) and Fowler (1954) because of their availability.

For behavioral observations see Reid and Atz (1958), Myrberg (1965), Loiselle (1967) and Sprenger (1970). Species of *Geophagus* exhibit all forms of cichlid egg incubation, from typical substratum care to immediate mouthbrooding. All of these "earth-eaters" are medium to large cichlids, typically diggers and uprooters, and should have large aquaria with sand or gravel and outside filtration. Breeding is sometimes induced in communities, but male:female aggression may inhibit breeding if only a pair is set up in its own aquarium, as Atz has noted.

The genus ranges from Panama in Central America all the way to Argentina in South America. The taxonomy is still in a state of confusion and the genus needs revision. The following notes on species are from the literature and from cursory observations of some pickled specimens at the American Museum of Natural History in New York.

G. jurupari and *G. acuticeps* are very similar to one another. Some time ago Innes indicated that the latter species could be distinguished from the former by its long, pointy ventrals, and I accepted that criterion in my earlier writings. However, Dr. James Atz has pointed out that both he and Myers have found this distinction not to hold up, as *G. jurupari* may also have such development of the ventral fins. I could not find any apparent differences glancing over preserved specimens of both species. Aquarists are thus advised to continue to use the name *G. jurupari* for aquarium strains of this type of fish. *G. jurupari* has a dark marking at the upper end of the caudal peduncle, and its facial markings vary from spots and blotches to streaks of iridescent material. Whether these facial markings are sexual, geographic, species-specific or random traits is not presently known. *G. jurupari* is a delayed mouthbrooder. Spawning occurs usually in a pit, and the eggs are picked up for oral incubation some twelve hours later.

These young specimens of *Geophagus jurupari* do not differ greatly from the adults. Photo by Dr. Herbert R. Axelrod.

Geophagus jurupari, adult. Photo by Dr. Herbert R. Axelrod.

The eye-to-mouth bands stand out clearly in this photo of *Geophagus jurupari*, as do the spot at the base of the caudal fin and the dark barring on the body. Photo by Dr. Herbert R. Axelrod.

Geophagus surinamensis gets more beautiful with age. The horizontal lines are characteristic, as is the blotch on the side. In small specimens, the eyes seem to be somewhat protuberant. This big fellow has his color pattern well developed. Photo by Dr. Herbert R. Axelrod.

G. surinamensis was imported into the United States only a few years ago, but it is already a very common species here. The head profile is convex, but there is a concave dip over the eyes, giving these fish a bug-eyed appearance. There is a mid-lateral dark blotch, which is usually intense. A series of iridescent green lines passe horizontally along the body, and this intensifies with age. Older males, especially, show a red flush to the unpaired fins. This fish is also a delayed mouthbrooder. The Florida fish farms frequently ship this fish as *jurupari*, erroneously.

G. brasiliensis is a typical substratum brooder, and doesn't resemble the preceding species in overall appearance in any way. *G. brasiliensis* inhabits the Amazon River drainage and lacks the long face so characteristic of other earth-eaters. It has a mid-lateral blotch and nacreous spotting. This spotting intensifies with age to form a dense pattern of pearly markings and the overall effect is reminiscent of the Texas cichlid, *Cichlasoma cyanoguttatum*. It attains large size and is easily bred.

Geophagus pellegrini, the redhump with the unusual breeding habits. Photo by Paul V. Loiselle.

G. pellegrini is known to be a mouthbrooder, but the timing has not been documented. The male develops a large nuchal hump or crest. Preserved specimens have a mid-lateral blotch of considerable size, and about seven light vertical bands. It has the long-nosed look of *G. jurupari.*

Sprenger (1971) reported the spawning of a *Geophagus* new to the hobby which she dubbed the redhump *Geophagus*. The male of this species develops a large red nuchal hump and, most interesting, there is no delay in mouthbrooding. The fish picks up its eggs immediately upon spawning much as do the African mbuna. Because of its prominent crest and the fact that it is a mouthbrooder I am tempted to consider this fish identical to *G. pellegrini* on the basis of present, albeit limited, information. Only an examination of pickled specimens of Sprenger's fish will help clear up the situation, and aquarists with pickled specimens of any (but especially this) *Geophagus* are advised to send them to Dr. Atz at the American Museum of Natural History, New York City 10024, U.S.A.

A fish new to the hobby and not yet reported as bred in the aquarium literature is also being shipped out of Florida as *jurupari*. It has three dark blotches on each side, with the last one very large, ocellated, and prominent on the upper part of the caudal fin. It closely resembles preserved specimens of *G. daemon*, even though *G. daemon* does not show the middle blotch very clearly in preservative.

Preserved specimens of *G. balzanii* are very distinct and I am certain that this fish has never been documented in the hobby. There is a blunt profile and about seven to eleven *pairs* of thin, dark bands on each side. This double-zebra striping is very distinctive. In addition, one finds a mid-lateral blotch and very dark pelvic fins.

Museum specimens of *G. crassilabrus* have the long nose and mid-lateral blotch so common to many species of *Geophagus*. There is a tendency for the presence of a horizontal dark band from the gill cover to the mid-lateral blotch. Overall the fish is dark in preservative, which means nothing. Bands are present, and there is a tendency for a nuchal hump to develop. The lips are thick.

G. hondae Regan is a poorly known and rather nondescript fish. It has a mid-caudal blotch and thick lips as in *G. crassilabrus*.

Geophagus balzanii. The double banding is characteristic of this species of South American cichlid. Photo by Dr. Herbert R. Axelrod.

Geophagus daemon. Photo by Dr. Herbert R. Axelrod.

Acarichthys heckelii, with the juvenile shown above and the adult below. This fish is now becoming common in the hobby. Photos by Harald Schultz.

G. brachyurus was illustrated by Fowler (1954) and I have seen preserved specimens. The mid-lateral blotch tends to extend downward, forming almost a black vertical bar.

Preserved specimens of *G. steindachneri* have a long nose, vertical banding, no mid-lateral blotch, but a spot at the middle of the caudal peduncle. The fins are spotted.

We have little information on *G. australe.* The type specimens were destroyed in an accident some time ago.

One Florida fish farm is breeding a *brasiliensis*-type of fish which was originally collected east of Bogota, Colombia. My guess is that this is *G. wavrini*, reported from that area. Typical substratum brooder, according to the breeder, and breeding occurs at a small size. Not yet released to the public.

SPECIES OF *GEOPHAGUS* HECKEL

	D	A	LL
G. acuticeps Heckel, 1840	XIII–XIV/11–12	III/7–8	30–31
G. australe Eigenmann, 1907	XII–XIV/10–11	III/8	25–27
G. balzanii Perugia, 1891	XIII–XIV/13	III/9	31
G. brachyurus Cope, 1894	XII–XIV/9–10	III/8	—
G. brasiliensis (Quoy & Gaimard, 1824)	XIV–XVI/10–13	III/8–9	27–30
G. camopiensis Pellegrin, 1903	XV–XVI/11–12	III/7	30–31
G. crassilabrus Steindachner, 1877	XV–XVI/10–11	III/7–8	30–31
G. daemon Heckel, 1840	XIII–XIV/11–14	III/8	32–33
G. gymnogenys Hensel, 1870	XIII–XIV/10–11	III/9	27–30
G. jurupari Heckel, 1840	XV–XVI/9–10	III/6–7	29–31
G. mapiritensis Fernandez-Yepez, 1950	XVI/8–9	III/7	30–31
G. pellegrini Regan, 1912	XVII/XVIII/9–11	III/7–9	31–34
G. steindachneri Eigenmann & Hildebrand, 1910	XV–XVII/10	III/8	—
G. surinamensis (Bloch, 1791)	XVII–XIX/11–13	III/7	33–36
G. wavrini Gosse, 1963	XIV–XV/10–12	III/9–10	27–30

THE GENUS *ACARICHTHYS*

Acarichthys Eigenmann, 1912 is a monotypic genus established by Eigenmann to contain the single species *A. heckelii* (Müller and Troschel, 1848). This fish has been the source of considerable confusion. Its synonyms include *Acara heckelii, Geophagus thayeri, Acara subocularis,* and *Aequidens subocularis.* (Please note that *Aequidens thayeri* is not a synonym, but a distinct and valid

Geophagus daemon is now commonly imported and should be easily recognized even when young. Photo by Paul V. Loiselle.

species.) There is a feebly developed lobe on the first gill arch, and about two gill rakers located at the base. It looks very much like a *Geophagus*, but probably is more akin to the more southerly *Retroculus*. *Acarichthys heckelii* was reported by Lowe-McConnell (1969) from Guyana. Its range also includes the Peruvian Amazon and into Brazil. Breeding habits are unknown. Stomach analysis by Lowe-McConnell indicated omnivorous feeding habits.

Biotodoma cupido above and below, showing two common color patterns. Photo above by H. Hansen, photo below by Harald Schultz.

Aequidens curviceps, pair with eggs. Photo by Ruda Zukal.

GENERA ALLIED TO *GEOPHAGUS*: *BIOTODOMA* AND *RETROCULUS*

Biotodoma cupido (Heckel, 1840) is thought to be a mouth-brooder, and was reviewed in the aquarium literature by Loiselle (1967). It has recently become readily available, and may be recognized by the black-on-white ocellus on the lateral line below the soft dorsal. The fins are clear. A dark stripe runs from the top of the head, through the rear part of the eye, to the lower angle of the operculum.

Retroculus lapidifer (Castelnau, 1855) is shaped much like a marine snapper (genus *Lutjanus*), and has five very distinct vertical bands on each side. It is a substratum breeder, at least at first. Castelnau described how this fish carried pebbles in its mouth to form a nest in which the eggs were laid (cited in Reid and Atz, 1958). *Retroculus* is separated from *Geophagus* by the structure of its gill rakers and their position on the base of the lobe of the first gill arch. In *Geophagus* these gill rakers, when developed, run onto the free edge of the lobe.

Recently Gosse (1971) reviewed the genus *Retroculus* and described two new species. The similarity among all three nominal species is extreme, and aquarists are not likely to be able to distinguish among them without knowing the original locality of the specimens. From Gosse's figures, the relationship of *Retroculus* to *Geophagus* is readily apparent, and it is not at all unlikely that one or more species have been occasionally imported but not recognized.

	D	A	L1	
R. lapidifer	XVI/11	III/6	29/23: 41	Brazil
R. xinguensis	XVII/11	III/6	33/22: 46	Rio Xingu
R. septentrionalis	XV/12	III/6	27/25: 40	Guyanas
B. cupido	XV/9–10	III/9	29–31	Guyanas

THE GENUS *AEQUIDENS*

The genus *Aequidens* Eigenmann and Bray, 1894 has long been a source of difficulty when compared with *Cichlasoma*. Aquarists are already familiar with the rule of thumb distinction: three anal spines for *Aequidens* and four or more for *Cichlasoma*. Unfortunately this distinction is not sufficient, for problems arise with other fishes. For example, there is evidence that *Aequidens portalegrensis* may have more than three anal spines in some of its populations, and that the aquarium "port" may actually be *Cichlasoma bimaculatum*. But this is still not clearly understood, and aquarists are advised to stick with the name *A. portalegrensis* until a substantial study settles the problem one way or the other. The teeth are of some value in distinguishing most *Cichlasoma* from most *Aequidens*, but again the division is not absolute. Generally the teeth in *Aequidens* are all conical, while some of the teeth in *Cichlasoma* may be enlarged to form canines. In fact, the name *Aequidens* translates to *equal teeth*.

Aequidens paraguayensis has recently been imported and bred. It is known to be a mouthbrooding species. Photo by G. Marcuse.

Aequidens curviceps. Photo by Ruda Zukal.

Aequidens hercules. Photo by Dr. Herbert R. Axelrod.

Aequidens maroni, the keyhole cichlid. A very shy species, not readily bred. Photo by Ruda Zukal.

Aequidens itanyi female with the ovipositor showing as she lays her eggs. Photo by Ruda Zukal.

In general, then, the characteristics of *Aequidens* may be listed as: gill arches without a lobe, small gill rakers, small and moderately protractile mouth, low lateral line, lateral line scales being of the same size as the other scales, three anal spines, soft dorsal and anal naked or scaled at the base only, lower lip without a frenum, teeth equal and no canine teeth.

These are generally considered medium sized cichlids, containing some large species (*portalegrensis, rivulatus*) and some relative dwarfs (*hercules, curviceps*). Many are distinctively marked, while others are very similar in markings, especially during fright phases. Young specimens are often difficult to identify. A number of species, not yet identified by aquarists, are established in the hobby.

Most species of *Aequidens* are not plant uprooters, and may be kept in tanks with large Amazon sword plants. There are few mouthbrooders known; most appear to spawn (at least in aquaria) on hard substrata. They should be provided with rockwork for hiding and territory marking. Only the larger species,

Aequidens rivulatus, the green terror. Photo of this male fish by Paul V. Loiselle.

Aequidens geayi, female. Photo by Paul V. Loiselle.

such as ports, should be considered diggers. Another name for this fish of bygone popularity is the black acara. As a matter of fact, *Acara* is the old (no longer valid) genus name for *Aequidens*. It was invalidated by Eigenmann and Bray when they found that the name of the type species of *Acara* was a synonym of *Astronotus ocellatus*. Regan didn't think much of this reasoning, and simply pulled all the non-*Aequidens* out of *Acara*, setting them into proper genera, and reserving the use of *Aequidens* for the remainder. *Aequidens* was the better name to use, because *Acara* had come to mean too many things to too many people.

Within this genus (as presently constituted) one finds all grades of difficulty or ease of breeding. The port is among the easiest of cichlids to spawn, while *A. thayeri*, *A. rivulatus* and *A. geayi* are difficult. Counts are meaningless in a genus of this size, and it will suffice to present various illustrations, plus a list of species and their native regions. In general, the genus is found in the headwaters of the Amazon in northern and western South America. Some species occur well into central South America and one species, *A. coeruleopunctatus*, occurs up into Middle America.

An as yet unidentified species of *Aequidens*. Photo by Harald Schultz.

Aequidens tetramerus, juvenile, in an atypical color phase. Photo by Harald Schultz.

Another unidentified species of the genus *Aequidens*. Photo by A. van den Nieuwenhuizen.

Aequidens thayeri grows to a large size. Photo by Dr. R. J. Goldstein.

For all but the easy species, artificial incubation of the eggs is recommended. The fishes should have quite clean water, and under these conditions are hardy, although not as vigorous as species of *Cichlasoma*. *Aequidens* species are generally not as aggressive as species of *Cichlasoma*, and are likely to be damaged or killed if mixed with rougher fishes, unless they are the larger fishes in the aquarium.

The newest species in the hobby are *Aequidens geayi* (see Goldstein, 1969 and Angier, 1970), a fish not yet reported as bred; *A. rivulatus* (see Goldstein, 1970), a fish which has been bred by a few people and which has been dubbed the green terror; and *A. thayeri* (see Advanced Aquarists Magazine number 24, 1971, cover photo), which has infrequently been bred.

The breeding behavior of *A. portalegrensis* has been documented by Greenberg, Zijlstra and Baerends (1965). The sticky head glands of the fry have been studied by Brinley and Eulberg (1953).

Aequidens portalegrensis, the black acara. Photo by Laurence E. Perkins, F.Z.S.

Aequidens itanyi, the dolphin cichlid from northeastern South America. Photo by Hilmar Hansen, Aquarium Berlin.

The species of *Aequidens* include the following, with synonyms in parentheses: *awani, biseriatus, coeruleopunctatus, curviceps, dorsigerus, duopunctatus, filamentosus, flavilabrus, freniferus, geayi, guianensis, guaporensis, hercules, hoehnei, itanyi, mariae, maronii, metae, minutus, paraguayensis, planifrons, portalegrensis, potaroensis, pulchra (=latifrons), rivulatus (=aequinoctialis, =azurifera), sapayensis, stollei, syspilus, tetramerus, thayeri, vittatus,* and *zamorensis.*

The general distribution is as follows: Panama and Costa Rica—*coeruleopunctatus;* Ecuador—*coeruleopunctatus, flavilabrus, rivulatus, vittatus, sapayensis, tetramerus* and *zamorensis;* Northwestern South America—*hercules, vittatus, freniferus, mariae, dorsigerus* and *tetramerus;* Venezuela—*tetramerus* and *pulchra* and expect (Schultz, 1949) *metae, mariae, vittatus* and *potaroensis.*

Note that *pulchra* is the correct spelling of the fish generally called *pulcher* in the U.S.A. and *latifrons* in Europe. Also known as the blue acara.

Aequidens pulchra, the blue acara. Photo of a specimen from the Rio Aguaro by Dr. Herbert R. Axelrod.

Aequidens rivulatus, the green terror. Photo by Dr. Robert J. Goldstein.

Aequidens pulchra, the blue acara in brooding coloration. Note the numerous fry. Photo by Kassanyi Jeno.

MERISTICS FOR SPECIES OF *AEQUIDENS* EIGENMANN & BRAY

	Dorsal	Anal	Ll
awani Haseman, 1911	XV/10	III/8	24–26
biseriatus (Regan, 1913)	XV–XVI/10	III/8	22–25
coeruleopunctatus (Kner & Steindachner, 1863)	XIV–XV/10–11	III/8–9	26–28
curviceps (Ahl, 1924)	XV/7	III/7	23–24
dorsigerus (Heckel, 1840)	XIII–XIV/7–10	III/7	23–24
duopunctatus Haseman, 1911	XV/9–11	III/7	26
filamentosus (Lacépède, 1802)	—	—	—
flavilabrus (Cope, 1870)	XVI/9–10	III/7	24
freniferus (Cope, 1872)	XVI/10–11	III/8	28–29
geayi (Pellegrin, 1902)	XIV–XV/9–11	III/8	26–27
guianensis (Regan, 1905)	XIII/10	III/7	25
guaporensis Haseman, 1911	XV/9	III/7	25
hercules Allen, 1942	XVI–XVII/8	III/6–7	26–29
hoehnei (Ribeiro, 1918)	XIV/9	III/8	—
itanyi Puyo, 1943	—	—	—
mariae Eigenmann, 1922	XIV/9–10	III/7–8	—
maronii (Steindachner, 1882)	XV/10–11	III/9–11	22–24
metae Eigenmann	XIV–XV/11–12	III/8–10	—
minutus (Hensel, 1870)	—	—	—
paraguayensis Eigenmann & Kennedy, 1903	XIII–XV/9–10	III/6–8	24–26
planifrons (Kaup, 1860)	—	—	—
portalegrensis (Hensel, 1870)	XV/10	III/9	24–26
potaroensis Eigenmann, 1912	XIV/9–10	III/7–8	—
pulchra (Gill, 1858)	XIV/10	III/8	23–25
rivulatus (Günther, 1859)	XII–XIV/11	III/8–9	25
sapayensis (Regan, 1903)	XIV–XV/10–11	III/9	24–25
stollei Ribeiro, 1918	—	—	—
syspilus (Cope, 1872)	XIV–XV/9–10	III/7–8	26–27
tetramerus (Heckel, 1840)	XV–XVI/10	III/8–10	26–27
thayeri (Steindachner, 1875)	XIV–XV/9–10	III/7	23–24
vittatus (Heckel, 1840)	XIII–XIV/10–11	III/7–8	24–26
zamorensis (Regan, 1905)	XIII–XIV/9–10	III/7–9	27

THE GENUS *ASTRONOTUS*

There are two species of the genus *Astronotus* Swainson, 1839. The one that is virtually unknown to the hobby is *A. orbicularis* of the Amazon. Well-known to all aquarists is the popular oscar, *A. ocellatus* (also of the Amazon, particularly the Rio Negro).

The genus is also a derivative of the Aequidens Group, having three anal spines. Additional generic characters include an entire preoperculum, the absence of a downward-projecting lobe on the

This young oscar, *Astronotus ocellatus,* looks quite different from the adult (see photo below). Photo by Dan Sonye.

Adult oscars require a large spacious aquarium. Note the smaller cichlid below the oscar on the left. Photo by Paul Zanalini.

The amount of red or orange exhibited in different oscars varies considerably. Photo by Dr. Herbert R. Axelrod.

first gill arch, and the soft parts of the vertical fins covered with small scales. The overall small scales on the body and much of the finnage has given rise to another common name for *A. ocellatus,* the velvet cichlid.

The oscar is a large fish requiring considerable tank space and heavy filtration; it can be a filthy animal to maintain at mature sizes of six to ten inches or more, largely because of its tendency

The normal color pattern of an adult oscar, *Astronotus ocellatus*. Photo by Klaus Paysan.

Young oscars such as these can be purchased at a relatively low price in pet shops. Adults are considerably more expensive. Photo by Harald Schultz.

to chew and spit its food. It becomes quite tame and makes a good pet.

Breeding usually occurs in the open on a hard surface, and the eggs tend to be laid in broad concentric circles. Spawns are quite large. Oscars are excellent parents and artificial incubation is generally unnecessary. The young grow rapidly and are marked differently from the parents, being generally dark-bodied with considerable marbling. At about three inches the adult coloration begins to appear, the fish becoming lighter and somewhat brownish green.

A recent introduction is the domestic red oscar, a fish with large amounts of orange pigmentation. The so-called tiger oscar seems to be a culled derivative of this strain.

The common oscar has become established in the waterways of southern Florida, where it is appreciated by fly-fishermen as the peacock-eye bass, a name sometimes also applied to *Cichla ocellaris*.

THE *CICHLASOMA* GROUP DERIVATIVES

This group contains those derivatives of the early Aequidens Group that went on to develop more than three anal spines. This line leads to *Cichlasoma* (including *Herichthys*), *Petenia* (now considered monotypic), *Herotilapia* (very close to *Cichlasoma* except for its teeth), *Neetroplus, Uaru, Pterophyllum* and *Symphysodon*.

THE GENUS *NEETROPLUS*

Neetroplus Günther, 1869 contains the following species:

N. nematopus Günther, 1869 Costa Rica and Nicaragua
N. panamensis Meek and Hildebrand, 1923 Panama
N. carpintis Jordan & Snyder, 1901 Mexico*

The genus is characterized by truncate, incisor-like teeth, and the body shape is typically *Cichlasoma*-like. There is a good likelihood that *N. carpintis* is either invalid or belongs to another genus, for it was not considered in Miller (1966), although that author pointed out that the other two species occur in the San Juan Province (a region made up of parts of Costa Rica, Nicaragua and Panama, at the southern end of middle America), quite far removed from Mexico. In this book, I am considering *carpintis* a questionable name; hence it is starred.

THE GENUS *UARU*

There are two distinct species of *Uaru* Heckel, 1840, in my opinion, despite Regan's (1905) synonymy of them. The most commonly seen species is *U. amphiacanthoides*, which has different shapes and colors at different sizes. The less commonly seen species is *U. imperialis*, the adults of which somewhat resemble the juveniles of the other species.

Uaru amphiacanthoides, one of the two species of the genus. Photo by G. Marcuse.

Herotilapia multispinosa is a *Cichlasoma* in every respect except for its tricuspid teeth, hence the separate generic category. Photo by Dr. Herbert R. Axelrod.

Uaru amphiacanthoides, juveniles. Photo by Dr. Herbert R. Axelrod.

Uaru amphiacanthoides, above and below, half-grown. Photos by G. Marcuse.

Herotilapia multispinosa. Photo by Dr. Robert J. Goldstein.

There are more than three anal spines, the teeth are slender and compressed, the scales are small, and the lateral line scales are larger than the other scales.

Young *Uaru amphiacanthoides* are almost disc-shaped, with considerable dirty brown markings. At about three inches the body begins to become more elongate, and the coloration becomes cleaner, with an overall blue-gray to brown-gray cast, subtle iridescence, and a large black patch on the lower body and root of the tail. Adult *U. imperialis* elongate somewhat, but retain the dirty brown markings. They are more orange-brown than iridescent gray.

Uaru are gentle fishes, stately and deliberate in their movements. They are not delicate, despite their behavioral similarities to discus. Breeding is in angel-discus fashion, generally off the bottom of the aquarium, but breeding reports are few. The fry are difficult to raise, and perhaps require parental slime to some extent. *Uaru* species are still rather expensive and, for this reason and because of their gentle nature, should be given a tank of their own.

THE GENUS *HEROTILAPIA*

Herotilapia Pellegrin, 1904 contains the single species *H. multispinosa* (Günther, 1869). In many respects it is closely related to *Cichlasoma nigrofasciatum*, but it is placed in its own genus because its teeth are tricuspid and compressed, except the middle outer teeth, which are truncate incisors (Regan, 1908). It is known from Costa Rica and from the Great Lakes of Nicaragua, i.e., the San Juan Province at the southern end of Middle America. The aquarium stock was sent here only a few years ago by Dr. William Bussing, who also sent *Cichlasoma centrarchus*.

The rainbow cichlid is quite easy to breed, and may do so at the tender size of an inch and a half. It attains at least four inches in length, and is relatively non-belligerent with fishes its own size. Many individuals, especially females, may be overall gray in body color until nuptial activity begins for the first time. At this time the dark golden color develops, and usually remains throughout life. Other individuals begin and remain gold, never going through an extended gray phase. Black blotches or vertical stripes occur on the flanks, and the pattern is quite variable. A popular and readily available species, especially recommended for beginners.

THE GENUS *PTEROPHYLLUM*

Pterophyllum Heckel, 1840 is a derivative of the *Cichlasoma* line of American cichlids characterized by more than three anal spines. The characteristics include a disc-shaped body with pointy snout, great development of the dorsal and anal fin rays and their associated membranes, and modification of the pelvic fins into long streamers. In the aquarium hobby, species of *Pterophyllum* are commonly called angelfishes.

The validity of the generic name has recently been challenged. Gery (1969) indicated that this generic name was illegally used, because it had been preoccupied by another genus of animals, and the next name in line to replace *Pterophyllum* was *Plataxoides* (resembling *Platax*, the marine batfishes). However, Gery failed to take note of a paper by Schultz (1967) which cleared up the situation. The name, according to Schultz (who was quoting

Pterophyllum scalare with its most typical color pattern. Photo by Klaus Paysan.

The gold blush angelfish was developed by John Gonzalez, Ed's Tropical Aquarium. Photo by J. Miklosz.

Myers), used for that earlier group of animals was actually *Pterophylla,* and this minute difference was sufficient to render *Pterophyllum* legal for the cichlid genus, as Heckel used it in 1840.

For a very long time the only angelfish in the hobby was known commonly as the scalare, which was a colloquialism for *Pterophyllum scalare,* the name then in use by aquarists. In 1953 Schultz reported that there were three angelfishes in the hobby, *P. scalare, P. eimekei,* and *P. altum.* He considered *P. eimekei* to be the commonly available aquarium angelfish. However, he has since studied additional material and come up with different conclusions. He now considers *P. scalare* and *P. eimekei* to be one and the same species, with the older name *P. scalare* taking priority. He also considers valid two additional species, *P. altum* and *P. dumerilii.* There is a possibility that *P. altum* may turn out to be an upper Orinoco subspecies of *P. scalare. P. dumerilii* occurs in the

One of the strains developed from the basic angelfish is this long-finned variety. Photo by Dr. Herbert R. Axelrod.

The black angelfish. A veiltailed variety of this strain is also available. Photo by Gunter Senfft.

same waters with *P. scalare* in the central and upper Amazon, but is characterized by a dark blotch at the base of the spiny dorsal on the body. *Plataxoides leopoldi* Gosse, 1963 is just a synonym of *Pt. dumerilii*. See the photos for the minute differences among these nominal species. In short, the species of the genus are very similar to one another, and *P. scalare* (Lichtenstein, 1823) is the common, albeit variable, species of aquarists. The other species are *P. altum* Pellegrin, 1903 and *P. dumerilii* (Castelnau, 1855).

The beginner tends to think of angels as difficult to keep, *ergo*, difficult to breed. Nothing could be further from the truth. Because of their bizarre and lovely form, the beginner will choose angels as among his first fishes in the hobby. And he will lose them, as he will lose his livebearers, tetras, catfishes, etc. But these losses are to be expected due to the nature of the aquarist's stage of development. All beginners lose fishes in their early days, and it is from these losses that the aquarist learns about water conditions, control of the tank environment, which fishes may be safely kept together and which may not. It is a learning period, and errors are documented in fish deaths. The aquarist may then think that all

Pterophyllum dumerilii normally has a spot at the base of the dorsal fin (as in this photo) rather than a vertical bar. Photo by Dr. Herbert R. Axelrod.

Pterophyllum altum, the long-finned angelfish from the Orinoco River. Photo by Dr. Herbert R. Axelrod.

these fishes he lost in his early days are hard to maintain, but that is not true once the aquarist has developed perspective and good habits. In terms of ease of care and breeding, the angelfish remains one of the best choices for the budding cichlidophile.

Angels tolerate a wide variety of water conditions and will thrive on a wide variety of prepared foods. Many breeders set up pairs in five-to fifteen-gallon tanks, bare, with an airstone or box filter and a strip of slate, plastic or other hard material on which to receive the spawns. Angels are best set up as one pair to an aquarium, and should be allowed to choose their own mates in a community set-up. Maturity is reached in less than a year with good care, but early spawns are not as productive as later ones. A pair can be identified in a community tank when it takes over a corner or a large leaf and drives off other fishes in the tank. At this time the fish should be removed to their own small spawning tank, and fed generously.

Both fish, but especially the female, will vigorously scrub the spawning site (slate, glass, plastic tube, plastic strip, etc.) with the mouth for about a week preceding spawning. About two days before actual spawning the breeding tubes of both will become very apparent. The male's tube is small, tapered and pointed slightly forward. The female's tube is broad, blunt, and rough-edged. Spawning may occur at any time of the day, and consists of the parents making alternate sweeps over the site chosen, depositing eggs in small groups, and milt.

The size of the spawn varies with the size, age and experience of the parent fishes. Bad eggs will turn opaque white in a couple of days, and these will rarely be removed by the parents. Instead, upon hatching the viable fry will be removed to another site previously prepared. Experienced angel pairs are generally good parents, but naive pairs frequently foul up the operation. Interestingly, if the eggs are removed from the parents upon spawning, they will likely spawn again in less than two weeks. And one can go through this removal-spawning-sequence for a great number of times before depleting the pair of their ability to produce quickly again. If you would like to see a lovely sight, you might allow the parents to attempt to raise the fry. A tank containing an angelfish family is a sight to remember.

Serious breeders get their kicks in other ways, and are concerned with cranking out as many angel babies as possible. Hence, they use the following method. Pairs are chosen from community tanks either by letting the fish choose their own mates, or by the breeder eyeballing a good male and a good female. (Parenthetic-

The half-black angelfish (above) and the marbled angelfish (below) were both developed from the normal angelfish, *Pterophyllum scalare*. Photos by Dr. Herbert R. Axelrod.

A young marbled angelfish. Photo by Hans J. Richter.

A cross between the normal silver angelfish and the black-lace angelfish resulted in this pattern. Photo courtesy of Lakeland Fish Hatcheries.

Angelfish can be housed in an aquarium with plants, unlike many other cichlids, which make a habit of uprooting them. Photo by Timmerman.

ally, almost any angel breeder can pick males and females from his own stock, but he cannot tell you how he knows. It is probably partly form, as the female tends to be stubbier than the male, and partly behavioral, as females tend to be more quick-acting.) Many angel breeders scoff at published reports of differences in belly profile, and I share their view.

Generally clean, somewhat alkaline and moderately hard tap water is used in the breeding tank, and no salt is added. The water is dechlorinated chemically (there is little point in storing water for ageing, as the chemicals are readily available and cheap), and persons who do large-scale breeding will either buy commercial dechlorinator in bulk or make up a solution of 65% sodium thiosulphite and use two or three drops per gallon. Tablets are too expensive to use. The staple diet will be blended or scraped beef heart, or live foods if they are cheap and readily available. Flake foods are a supplement only.

Upon spawning (which occurs at room temperature, and obviates the need for individual aquarium heaters) the hard substratum containing the eggs is removed and placed in a bucket or one-gallon wide-mouth jar with clean tank water (filtered if necessary). Liquid methylene blue (never the dry powder) is added sufficiently to darken the water until you can barely see your hand behind the jar. The water should be dark blue, and not sky blue. The jar is placed up on a table away from cold air, in order to keep the temperature fairly high (and not less than generally comfortable room temperature). An air stone is added near the eggs, but the bubbles should not skip directly on the eggs. Aeration should be fairly vigorous if more than a couple of inches from the eggs. An additional caution in very well lighted fish rooms is placing the whole jar or bucket inside a brown paper sack from the super market, to protect the eggs from bright light. Some people think the eggs are light sensitive, but very few bother with the paper bag routine. The eggs hatch in a few days, and the fry should now be squirted off the spawning strip onto the floor of the jar, and the spawning strip containing fungused patches of bad eggs removed from the jar. Keep the air stone removed from the floor of the jar by at least an inch.

After about another five days remove the stone momentarily and observe whether the fry are still sticking to one another and to the crud at the bottom of the jar, or if they are beginning to make short swimming forays up in the water. Once they have begun swimming, it is time to begin feeding live baby brine shrimp. Begin water changes at this time. When all the fry are eating and apparently strong (in about another week), they can be dumped into a rearing aquarium of about ten-gallon size.

For filtration, use an inside box filter filled with gravel only, or use one of the fine-pore biological or undergravel type filters (without any gravel). A cheap filter is an air release and air line which has been wrapped with foam rubber and tied with a rubber band. Feed copious amounts of live baby brine shrimp, and add some snails or catfish to clean up the uneaten food. As needed, you should split up the fry or move them to larger quarters. If you have several pairs of angels going at the same time, you can handle the fry together. Use very large aquaria with strong aeration and copious amounts of food for large numbers of juveniles, and maintain those water changes at an equal or greater frequency. Water changes and lots of living foods will give you a maximal growth rate.

The classical angel is the fish now called the silver angel, and it is hardier than the other types. There are long-finned kinds and there are many color varieties, including black, gray, blushing (a washed out fish that I wouldn't have in my own house), blue-over-blushing (this one isn't bad), marble (a rather pretty fish), gold (and this color takes almost a year to develop from normal appearing fry),* and albinos (which are thrown off by golds in small numbers and which apparently all go blind in a very short while). The black long-finned variety is the most difficult to maintain successfully, followed by the plain black. All the others [except for the albino which usually starves to death] are easily raised. Many breeders grow all their fry together, and separate fish only when they are taking them out for sale. I think long-finned types should be raised separately from short-finned types because of their lesser ability to get in there at the food.

The albino angel is the only animal I know that is born pigmented and becomes albinistic later in life. The physiology and genetics should prove to be most interesting, if the fish can just be kept alive.

* Except for Wong strain.

THE GENUS *SYMPHYSODON*

The genus *Symphysodon* Heckel, 1840 contains the discusfishes, disk-shaped, medium-sized cichlids with a long anal fin with seven or more spines (Lowe-McConnell, 1969). Two species are recognized; *S. discus* Heckel, 1840 in the Rio Negro and *S. aequifasciata* Pellegrin, 1903 in the Amazon. Schultz (1967) divided *S. aequifasciata* into a number of subspecies, but I find it difficult to accept his thesis, having information that the forms are habitat types, rather than geographic derivatives of a basic stock. Thus, I will accept distinct color types as associated with specific types of waters, and that these color forms breed true. But the thesis that they reflect the beginnings of speciation is not, in my opinion, tenable when applied to a region characterized by heavy rainfall, flooding, and mixing of waters. There are no behavioral isolating mechanisms known among the color forms. Meristic and morphometric differences, even between the two recognized species, are minute.

Symphysodon discus exhibiting the very dark central body bar. Photo by Hilmar Hansen.

Symphysodon discus from Brazil. The variable color patterns of these fishes make identification of the species very difficult. Photo by Wolfgang Bechtle.

A number of color forms of discus are available in the hobby, although the distinctions often break down due to natural variation and crossings. The terms brown and green discus are seldom used at present, and the use of blue discus is more and more restricted to the better strains. Perhaps the best blue strain available is Wattley's Turquoise discus, characterized by maximal development of the blue streaks over the entire body, rather than restricted largely to the head. Other strains are quite similar, and these strains were developed by breeding the best blue fish that these aquarists found in nature. Wattley's fish were collected far apart, and were brought together to breed for the blue color.

There are many other famous discus breeders in the U.S.A., such as Art Hayley and the late Carol Friswold. But few people, with the exception of Wattley and perhaps some others, have made the expeditions to South America where they collected and studied discus in the wild. To such aquarists the hobby owes a great debt. A new fish reported in the hobby is Günter Keller's bright red discus. I suspect that this color was induced by drugs, and is not genetic. Time will tell. This German strain is not yet available in the United States.

Discus ought to be kept in large aquaria at warm temperatures, not less than 80 to 82°F, and up to the mid-nineties under certain circumstances, as in the treatment of headworm or hole-in-the-head-disease (one and the same). The tank should be well planted around the back or one side, with a large open area in front. Various authors have different ideas on optimal pH values, ranging from slightly acid to slightly alkaline. All agree that massive and frequent water changes are imperative for maintaining these fish in good health. Most authors prefer soft water, but some believe in moderate hardness; very hard water is taboo, at least among those breeders who take the trouble to publish their views.

All discus breeders have their "secret formulas" for keeping the fish in good health and developing the best coloration. Most of these are based on some living foods supplemented with vegetables and beef heart. *Tubifex* worms are perfectly all right for discus and other fishes. Some aquarists have a tendency to blame tubificid worms (because of their occurrence in sewage) for outbreaks of disease, much as they will blame brine shrimp for outbreaks of white body malady in guppies or velvet in killies. In my opinion, all of these living foods are perfectly good for all tropical fishes which will eat them, and outbreaks of disease ought to be blamed on dirty tanks or failure to change water frequently and massively.

Discus are subject to one common and one rare malady of interest. The rare ailment is infection with *Artystone trysibia*, a parasitic isopod found in the body cavity of wild fishes on occasion. This massive pillbug-like creature eventually punctures the body wall of the host fish. It is found in other South American fishes as well. Findings of this parasite are only confirmed at autopsy, provided the aquarist will pickle the parasite in alcohol or formalin and send it to me or another parasitologist. If the parasite can be recovered alive, and shipped alive, that is even better. *Artystone* invariably kills the host discus, and treatment should not be considered. See Huizinga (1972).

A young discus is easily distinguishable, closely resembling the adult in shape and color pattern. Photo by Laurence E. Perkins.

Symphysodon aequifasciata approximately 2 years old. Photo by H. Hansen.

The bars of *Symphysodon aequifasciata* may be faded, as in this individual. Photo by D. Terver of the Nancy Aquarium, France.

The bars of this individual are very dark and of equal strength. Photo by Edward Schmidt.

The so-called hole-in-the-head disease (headworm disease) is of unknown etiology. Various sources have reported the findings of protozoa, fungi, or bacteria in the lesions. I have been unable to confirm any of these reports. The infection is characterized by a massive flow of exudate from lesions which originate along and within the lateral line system of the head. What stimulates this flow of exudate (a defense reaction) is unknown. The material is sterile (containing no bacteria or other forms of life), and I have been unable to find recognizable animal parasites or any kinds of fungi in sections of tissue from affected areas. Nonetheless, it does appear to be contagious and thus caused by a parasite of some kind. Treatments reported as successful include tetracyclines (indicating that bacteria are involved) and high heat (which stimulates the production of antibodies in fishes). Antiprotozoan drugs seem to be of no avail, and the same is true of antifungal drugs. The best all-round treatment is tetracyclines and a temperature of about 94°F, but which of these is actually responsible for helping the situation is presently unknown. I have found a fungus in liver sections from one discus fish, but this seems to be unrelated to any overt disease-induced behavior of the fish, which died from other causes.

Discus in good health will not develop their best colors or be likely to spawn until they are two years old or older. Old fish of three to five years appear to look good and reproduce with some regularity. Discus should have a tank of their own and should definitely not be kept with other cichlids. Spawning will occur on a strip of slate, a flowerpot, or any other hard surface removed from the bottom. Naive parents are likely to eat their eggs before hatching time, but older fish often do better. Discus fry feed on the slime secreted by the parents, much as do the fry of orange chromides, *Etroplus maculatus*.

Many discus breeders allow the parents to raise the fry, while others prefer artificial handling of the eggs and fry. Parental slime, as food for the fry, cannot be replaced by the usual fry foods and special handling is necessary. If the parents are allowed to keep the fry, the fish room should be undisturbed, and unnecessary visitors should be barred. Avoid rapid movements around the fish, as these are likely to induce (in both brooding and non-brooding discus) fright behavior manifested by wild dashing

An adult discus with the young feeding off the body mucus. Photo by Gerhard Budich.

One of the new strains of discus is this one with quite a bit of red coloration. Photos by Gunter Keller.

Another strain of discus but with an essentially green cast. Photo by Harald Schultz of wild specimens from Lake Tefé.

about, bumping of the head against the glass, and various other kinds of physical damage. Eggs and fry are very likely to be eaten.

Discus are for the patient aquarist who has the time and inclination to devote to them the very best of care, including cleanliness, water changes, constant monitoring of temperature, and careful rather than haphazard feeding. Discus do not tolerate any kind of laxity, and will go off their feed and often die under conditions that other kinds of cichlids would take in stride. On the other hand, many people succeed in killing them with what they consider kindness. The discus which is just not hungry today ought not to be bombarded with food and medication. Leave it alone. Many of us place great value on solitude, quiet, and a genteel way of life; discus ought to be treated the same way.

Some years ago Friswold developed a method of raising discus fry away from the parents, bypassing the requirement for parental slime. Recently, Vilda (1970) published a similar (but not identical) method, which is herein presented.

The slate or leaf containing the discus eggs is removed from the breeding tank and placed in a gallon jar containing tank water. Do not remove the eggs from the breeders any sooner than two hours post-spawning. Add acriflavine solution (not powder!) to the incubation jar, and maintain with aeration in dim light or in the dark at 80 to 82°F. The eggs will have mostly hatched in two to three days. At this time, pour the contents of the jar (water and fry) into an enamel pan about 16″ × 11″ × 5″. The pan should have gently sloping sides. Siphon off most of the water and all of the debris. Next, add equal parts (pre-mixed) of clean tank water and distilled water, always maintaining your 80 to 82°F temperature. Maintain aeration in the pan. The fry will adhere to each other, forming clumps of wigglers. In about a week they will break loose and begin to swim. Do not feed them yet! Wait at least five hours in order to allow the fry to completely resorb the yolk, which they will quickly do with the added energy demands of swimming. Anybody can get this far (and many have). But for the next five days you will be feeding and caring for your fry in a way that no other aquarium fishes require, and this is the trick to raising discus.

Get some commercial egg yolk from your bake shop. Place a small amount on some waxed paper and flatten it with your fingers to a thickness of about an eighth inch. Next, using your fingers, stick a dime-sized amount onto the sloping side of the pan, so that half is above and half is below the water line. Do this all around the pan at intervals of about two inches. Remove the air-lines from the pan. Allow the fry to feed for two hours. (Now that the fry are going to feed, you can set up a 25 watt light bulb about three feet above the pan. To maintain warm temperature, you can float the pan inside a large heated aquarium with a glass cover.)

After two hours, remove the fry from the pan, using a large-orifice glass syringe or a baster, and place them in a dish of clean water. Clean out your pan, and set it up once again with air lines and clean water. Put the fry back.

Repeat the feeding and cleaning ritual at least three, and preferably four or five, times a day for the next five days. On the sixth day the fry will be able to take newly hatched brine shrimp or microworms. Maintain temperature control and exceptional cleanliness, with water changes daily. Remove all uneaten food between feedings, which may now be reduced to twice a day. Once you've gotten the fry past the egg yolk stage and onto the brine shrimp regimen, you're practically home free. Discus, as with other cichlids, will breed more frequently if their eggs are removed. Art Hayley reported one pair that bred for a time at six-day intervals, but this is exceptional. Discus will breed at regular intervals for a considerable time, and then discontinue spawning for a long time. They are not ill, and with care will initiate another round of spawnings some time in the future. Do not push them with too much tender loving care in an effort to squeeze just one more spawning out of them.

THE GENUS *CICHLASOMA*

Cichlasoma Swainson, 1839, is the largest American genus of cichlids. Some authors have used the generic name *Cichlaurus* Swainson, 1839, but this is improper. Swainson used both names in his original paper, and the first revisor, following the rules of nomenclature, chose *Cichlasoma* to be retained and *Cichlaurus* to be rejected.

Definitions of *Cichlasoma* have changed a great deal over the years. For example, Jordan and Evermann defined the genus in

Cichlasoma octofasciatum, the Jack Dempsey. Incorrectly known in years past as *C. biocellatum*. See text. Photo by Dr. Wm. T. Innes.

Cichlasoma meeki, the firemouth cichlid, is a member of the *Thorichthys* section of *Cichlasoma*. Both the firemouth and the Jack Dempsey may be collected in Mexico. Photo by Ruda Zukal.

Cichlasoma festivum, a big, peaceful fish from quiet waters of South America. Photo by Dr. Herbert R. Axelrod.

Cichlasoma centrarchus, introduced to the hobby from Costa Rica by Dr. Bill Bussing. Body usually greenish-grey, but lavender when spawning and brooding fry. Photo by Dr. Robert J. Goldstein.

part as having four to eleven anal spines, dorsal and anal fins not closely scaled, and the lower lip interrupted in the middle to form a frenum. Regan (1906) went considerably further. In part, Regan included in his definition the following characters: jaws with bands of small conical teeth, the outer series more or less enlarged and sometimes forming canines; mouth small or moderate; premaxillary processes shorter than the head; maxillary exposed or not; upper surface of the head scaly to the level of the orbits or beyond; cheeks and opercular bones scaly; preoperculum entire; gillrakers short and few, with about six to fifteen on the lower part of the first gill arch; anal with IV or more spines, etc. It was Regan who laid the foundation for our understanding of *Cichlasoma* and other American cichlid genera and there has yet to be an analysis anywhere near as profound.

There are many nominal genera that today are considered synonyms of *Cichlasoma*. We have already mentioned *Cichlaurus*. Others are *Heros, Mesonauta, Herichthys, Paraneetroplus, Thorichthys, Archocentrus, Amphilophus* and *Parapetenia*. Some of these names, however, are still very useful as *sections* (not legal subgenera) of *Cichlasoma*, and this is how Regan and later authors

A truly magnificent specimen of *Cichlasoma managuense*, tank-raised. Photo by Paul V. Loiselle.

used them. In looking over the definition of the recently described genus *Chuco*, I suspect that this too might be included in *Cichlasoma*, but will wait for qualified ichthyologists to make that evaluation.

All species of *Cichlasoma* are apparently substratum brooders, with little sexual dimorphism or dichromatism. Males tend to be larger and with more pointed dorsal and anal fins, but this does not always hold true. Most of them seem to be able to attain very large size in public aquaria, with a tendency for males, especially, to develop a nuchal crest of fatty tissue. A strong pair bond forms prior to spawning, and most species are excellent guardians of the eggs and fry. Both the male and female prepare the spawning site, which may be a sand, gravel or mud pit, or a hard surface. Preparation of the spawning site takes several days, and the genital papillae extrude a few days before actual spawning. On the day of spawning the papillae are maximally extended. Spawns vary from a hundred to over a thousand eggs, depending on the size of the parents. Upon hatching, the fry are usually removed to another site, often a pit. (I have observed *Herotilapia*, which appears to be a *Cichlasoma* in every respect save its tricuspid teeth, place its fry in floating plants. But this may have been a response to a filthy tank bottom.) Very few breeders bother with artificial incubation of the eggs, because species of *Cichlasoma* are so predictably reliable as parents, and because spawns are large anyway. None of these fishes ought to be bred in community cichlid tanks, or a lot of severely damaged fishes will result.

A community tank of *Cichlasoma*, *Aequidens*, and other large forms is attractive, provided there is plenty of room and rockwork. Nothing less than a hundred gallons is really adequate for a group of these large fishes, unless one splits pairs. Species of *Cichlasoma* can be bred in outdoor pools during warm weather, and the offspring sold or used as food for other fishes. Earthworms and bait minnows are greedily taken and should be supplied by the loving aquarist. These fishes are exceptionally hardy and vigorous, however, and will tolerate the filthiest aquaria if the water is not allowed to foul.

The intelligence of these fishes is without parallel among all fishes known to the hobby, within the family and without. They are territorial and great diggers. In general the gentler species in

Cichlasoma friedrichsthalii, female. The female of this species is practically identical in markings to that of *C. dowi*. Photo by Dr. R. J. Goldstein.

Cichlasoma facetum, the chanchito. Preserved specimen. Photo by Dr. Herbert R. Axelrod.

Cichlasoma friedrichsthalii, male. The absence of triangular point markings on the flanks and of vermiculations on the face separates this species from the related *C. dowi* and *C. managuense.* Photo by Dr. R. J. Goldstein.

An unidentified Neotropical cichlid tentatively placed in the genus *Cichlasoma.* Photo by Dr. R. J. Goldstein.

the hobby, such as *C. festivum*, *C. severum*, and *C. hellebrunni* (often called *coryphaenoides* in the hobby) come from South America, whereas the vast majority of species of *Cichlasoma* (and also the most belligerent) are Central American. It has been suggested that belligerency increases as one approaches New York! Interestingly, the most belligerent species, and thereby the most territorial, usually make the best parents.

Before discussing some of these species of especial interest in the hobby, we ought to first say something about the general taxonomic arrangement of the genus. Then, we can discuss specific fishes within the framework of this scheme.

THE ORGANIZATION OF *CICHLASOMA*

Regan (1908) arranged *Cichlasoma* into five sections which he felt were natural groups; he did not consider these groups sufficiently distinct to merit subgeneric rank. Miller (1966) used seven sections, incorporating groups of species that earlier authors had given generic rank. I will use Miller's scheme here, and refer to Regan's criteria.

A few words about fish provinces are in order. This is essential to appreciating the distribution of Central American species. In this discussion I shall combine Regan's ideas with Miller's modifications. At the southern end of Middle America is Panama. Just to the northwest is Costa Rica. Panama and parts of Costa Rica make up the Isthmian Province. According to Miller (1966), "*. . . a fish province is a region that is characterized by groups of associated species that have similar geographic and ecologic ranges. Endemism is marked . . .*". These fish provinces are somewhat set off by geologic barriers, such as mountains, deserts or other inhibitors of dispersal.

Just to the northwest of the Isthmian Province is the San Juan Province, consisting of parts of Costa Rica and Nicaragua, and with its drainage emptying into the Atlantic. A very large provisional region was Regan's Guatemalan Province, which has been substantially modified by Miller into several smaller provinces. Extending along the Pacific slope and including the northern Pacific peninsula of Costa Rica is the Chiapas-Nicaraguan Province, which extends northward into parts of the southern

Cichlasoma dowi (also spelled *dovii*) is a member of the *Parapetenia* section of its genus, ranging from Costa Rica to Honduras. This large male was photographed by Paul V. Loiselle.

bulge of Mexico. Making up the large Usumacinta Province would be Yucatan, Guatemala and British Honduras. Most of the Atlantic bulge of Honduras and Nicaragua was unclassified by Miller, due to lack of data on fishes of the region (now being remedied). And now, the *Cichlasoma* sections will make more sense.

The first group is the section *Theraps*. This is a widely distributed and probably relatively primitive group, extending all the way from Mexico, through all the provinces, into Colombia of South America. Rather than go through the technical characteristics, which may be found in Regan (1908), I will merely list the species in hopes that some basic similarity will become apparent to aquarists. The species are: *eigenmanni* Meek, 1902; *nebuliferum* (Günther, 1860); *maculicauda* Regan, 1905 (which has a large dark blotch on the caudal peduncle); *melanurum* (Günther, 1862); *synspilum* Hubbs, 1935 (which *may* be the same as *melanurum* and is *known* to be the same as *hicklingi* Fowler); *fenestratum* (Günther, 1860); *sexfasciatum* Regan, 1905; *bifasciatum* (Steindachner, 1864); *heterospilum* Hubbs, 1935; *guttulatum* (Günther, 1864);

Cichlasoma spilurum. Photo by Ruda Zukal.

Cichlasoma nigrofasciatum, wild type. A gold strain is also available, known as the pink congo or pink convict. Photo by Ruda Zukal

Cichlasoma species, not yet identified. Photo by Dr. Herbert R. Axelrod.

Cichlasoma centrarchus. Photo by Dr. Herbert R. Axelrod.

godmani (Günther, 1862); *microphthalmum* (Günther, 1862); *gadowi* Regan, 1905; *intermedium* (Günther, 1962); *sieboldi* (Kner and Steindachner, 1864), which also includes Regan's *Herichthys underwoodi* according to Bussing; *irregulare* (Günther, 1862); *lentiginosum* (Steindachner, 1864); *balteatum* (Gill and Bransford, 1877), which may be the same as the next species; and *nicaraguense* (Günther, 1864). A number of additional species were listed by Regan in this section, but apparently are invalid or have been moved elsewhere, if one follows Miller's (1966) scheme, as presented here.

The section *Herichthys* comprises the species in the old genus *Herichthys* Baird and Girard, 1854. The outer series of teeth are generally compressed and enlarged, and the group is restricted to the Atlantic slope of Mexico, or the Usumacinta Province and northward into Texas. The species include: *bocourti* (Baillant and Pellegrin, 1902); *geddesi* Regan, 1905; *pearsei* (Hubbs, 1935); and *cyanoguttatum* (Baird and Girard, 1854), also known as the Texas cichlid or Rio Grande perch. For information on the latter see Schleser (1971).

Cichlasoma facetum, the chanchito. Female with ten-day-old free-swimming fry. Photo by Marcuse.

The next section was called *Astatheros* by Regan, but has been modified and now called *Amphilophus* by Miller (1966). This is a widespread group, with most species from northern Middle America. The species of *Cichlasoma* in this section include: *robertsoni* Regan, 1905, which also includes *acutum* Miller; *longimanus* (Günther, 1869); *macracanthum* (Günther, 1864), which also includes *heterodontum* Vaillant and Pellegrin as well as *evermanni* Meek; *altifrons* (Kner and Steindachner, 1863); *rostratum* (Gill and Bransford, 1877), a long-snouted fish with a blotch in the middle of the side below the lateral line, and colored bands in the soft portions of the unpaired fins; *popenoei* Carr and Giovannoli, 1950; *margaritiferum* (Günther, 1862); *citrinellum* (Günther, 1864); *erythraeum* (Günther, 1869), which may be the same as *citrinellum* or *labiatum* and commonly called red devils; *lobochilus* (Günther, 1869); *alfaroi* Meek, 1907 (also spelled *alfari*), and including *lethrinus* Regan; *labiatum* (Günther, 1864), possibly the same as *erythraeum*; and *tuyrense* Meek and Hildebrand, 1923.

Many of these species are found in the Great Lakes of Nicaragua, several of them have fleshy lips, and some undergo marked color changes as they grow. Whether the aquarium red devils represent one or several species is not yet known.

The section *Paraneetroplus* contains *C. bulleri* (Regan, 1905), from the Atlantic slope of southern Mexico. In general outline this fish is elongate, with a blunt head and low mouth. The overall appearance greatly resembles a *Pseudotropheus* species from Africa's Lake Malawi. A series of vertical dark blotches adorns the sides. The lower jaw is smaller than the upper, and all the teeth are compressed, with pointed or rounded tips. Usumacinta Province.

The section *Archocentrus* contains some familiar fishes. This is a small, but wide-ranging group. The body is deep, but the mouth is small. The species include: *spilurum* (Günther, 1862); *nigrofasciatum* (Günther, 1869); *octofasciatum* (Regan, 1903); *centrarchus* (Gill and Bransford, 1877); *immaculatum* Pellegrin, 1904; and *spinosissimum* (Vaillant and Pellegrin, 1902). The last two may represent the same species.

C. spilurum is occasionally seen in the hobby, but they have not been propagated sufficiently to become readily available. *C. nigrofasciatum* is the common congo or convict cichlid, one of the

The photos above and below show how different two specimens of the same species can appear. Both are *Cichlasoma severum*. Photo above by G. Marcuse; photo below by Dr. Herbert R. Axelrod.

A pair of young *Cichlasoma severum*.

Cichlasoma severum, golden strain. Photo by Barbara E. Marlay.

Petenia splendida, juvenile, from British Honduras stock. Photo by Paul V. Loiselle.

easiest and most prolific of all American cichlids. For a behavioral study, see Weber (1970). This has often been confused with *facetum*, a differently shaped and marked fish. A pink strain is available, developed by Ken Grisham of Fort Worth, Texas. This fish was claimed to be the product of two different fish farms, but it was Grisham who found the sports in his normal *nigrofasciatum* and succeeded in fixing the strain, which he then distributed to Dallas-Fort Worth aquarists and the Dallas Aquarium. From these sources, the fish spread rapidly and became one of the most popular of all cichlids. There were originally just two mutants in one spawning, and in 1962–1963 Grisham fixed the strain and distributed about 20 breeders. He then dropped out of the hobby for a time, and in 1968 moved to Canada. At this time he got into the hobby again, and was shocked to find that his own strain had beaten him to Canada! The so-called "cutteri" in the hobby is simply a color strain of *C. nigrofasciatum*. Legally, the name *C. cutteri* is a junior (invalid) synonym of *C. spilurum*.

C. octofasciatum is another interesting story. This is the correct name of the Jack Dempsey, an old favorite. It is native to the Atlantic slope from Yucatan, through Vera Cruz and into Honduras. For years it was known in the hobby as *biocellatum*, but it was suggested by Miller that *biocellatum* is the same as *octofasciatum* and Dr. G. S. Myers and Luis Rivas verified this, though their paper is still unpublished. *C. "biocellatum"* was a name that belonged to a "South American" species (non-existent), and they knew the Jack Dempsey was available as close as Mexico.

Cichlasoma centrarchus was recently introduced to the hobby through Dr. Bill Bussing.

Another large section, containing some species known in the hobby, is the section *Thorichthys*. This group was poorly known in Regan's day, and is considered much larger today by Miller. Most of the species are in the Usumacinta province, but several range downward into Costa Rica and one species reaches Panama. The *Thorichthys* group was treated in depth by Miller and Nelson (1961). The species include: *callolepis* (Regan, 1904), discussed in the Miller and Nelson paper in depth; *aureum* (Günther, 1862), the golden cichlid; *ellioti* Meek, 1908, which may be the same as the next species; *helleri* (Steindachner); *champotonis* Hubbs, 1936; *affine* (Günther, 1862); *meeki* (Brind, 1918), the firemouth; *hyorhynchum* Hubbs, 1935; *pasionis* Rivas, 1962. *C. hyorhynchum* has recently been released to the hobby by Dr. Jamie Thomerson.

The position, as to section, of another group is not clear. This group includes *calobrense* Meek and Hildebrand, 1923; *spilotum* Meek, 1908; *umbriferum* Meek and Hildebrand, 1923 and *terrabae* Jordan and Evermann, 1927. It is certain that *tuba* Meek does not belong in the *Thorichthys* section.

Eigenmann's (1924) system is not generally consonant with modern dispositions of species of *Cichlasoma*, but it is interesting to note that he placed the following species in his old group *Astatheros: festae* (Boulenger, 1899) from Ecuador; *ornatum* Regan, 1905 from Colombia and Ecuador; *atromaculatum* Regan, 1912 from Colombia and Panama; *altifrons* (now in *Amphilophus*); and *calobrense* from Panama.

Cichlasoma synspilum, young adult male pond-raised in Florida from British Honduras stock. Photo by Dr. R. J. Goldstein.

Cichlasoma citrinellum. Photo by Klaus Paysan.

Cichlasoma managuense. Photo by A. Norman

Cichlasoma managuense. As it grows, this fish will develop black markings and a blood red eye. Photo by Dr. R. J. Goldstein.

The *Parapetenia* section of *Cichlasoma* contains several fishes known in the hobby. This is another fairly large and widely ranging group of species. The mouth is generally large, and there are two enlarged, canine-like teeth in the front of the upper jaw. There are two canine-like teeth on each side of the middle teeth in the lower jaw. The upper profile of the snout is straight and the caudal is rounded. The species include: *mento* (Vaillant and Pellegrin, 1902) from southern Mexico's Rio Negro; *urophthalmus* (Günther, 1862), ranging from northern Yucatan through Guatemala, British Honduras, Honduras and into Nicaragua, and divided into several subspecies; *hogaboomorum* Carr and Giovannoli, 1950 from the Pacific slope of Honduras; *trimaculatum* (Günther, 1869), whose synonyms include *mojarra* Meek, *centrale* Meek, *gordonsmithi* Fowler and *cajali* Alvarez and Gutierrez, and recently introduced to the hobby; *tenue* Meek, 1908; *salvini* (Günther, 1864), newly reintroduced to the hobby; *friedrichsthali* (Heckel, 1840), widely ranging along the Atlantic slope from Mexico to Costa Rica; *managuense* (Günther, 1869); *myersi* (Schultz, 1944)

Cichlasoma spilotum, female. Known only from Costa Rica. Photo by Paul V. Loiselle.

from Colombia; *spectabile* (Steindachner, 1875) from Colombia; *dowi* (Günther, 1864), also called *dovii* and ranging from Costa Rica northward into Honduras; *motaguense* (Günther, 1869), which may be the same as *friedrichsthali*; and *kraussii* (Steindachner, 1879) from Colombia and Venezuela, introduced to the hobby in 1970. *C. kraussii* feeds on small animal life (e.g., adult brine shrimp in aquaria) by telescoping its jaws into a long tube.

For aquarium information on *trimaculatum* see AAA Newsletter (Atlanta) #18 (Nov., 1970); for *dowi* see Olson (1970); and for *friedrichsthali* see Olson and Gianladis (1970a and 1970b); for several species compared see Gianladis and Olson (1970).

Since the South American species of *Cichlasoma* were not treated in Miller (1966), it is necessary to fall back on Regan's (1905) classification for such forms. Because the species of *Cichlasoma* are fewer and their specific ranges wider, I prefer simply to list the species with their general distribution. Obviously the structure of *Cichlasoma* does not present the problems in South America which are seen farther north. The following data are from various authors:

C. bimaculatum (Linnaeus, 1754)	Brazil, Guianas, Trinidad
C. festivum (Heckel, 1840)	Brazil, Guianas
C. facetum (Jenyns, 1842)	Argentina
C. autochthon (Günther, 1862)	Eastern Brazil
C. oblongum (Castelnau, 1855)	Southern and Eastern Brazil, Argentina
C. temporale (Günther, 1862)	Brazil, Guianas
C. coryphaenoides (Heckel, 1840)	Brazil
C. severum (Heckel, 1840)	Brazil, Guianas
C. psittacum (Heckel, 1840)	Brazil, North Atlantic S.A.
C. festae (Boulenger, 1899)	Ecuador
C. ornatum Regan, 1905	Ecuador
C. hellebrunni Ladiges, 1942	Upper Amazon Basin

Island species of *Cichlasoma* include:

C. adspersum (Günther, 1862)*	Barbados
C. tetracanthum (Cuv. & Valenc., 1831)**	Cuba, Haiti, Dominican Republic
C. ramsdeni Fowler, 1938	Cuba

*May be *C. tetracanthum* introduced to Barbados, or a locality error.
**Synonym: *C. haitiensis* Tee-Van, 1935.

Cichlasoma temporale, previously known as *C. crassa*. It occurs in South America, along with the closely related *C. coryphaenoides* and *C. hellebrunni,* and the relationship among this group of species is very close. Some aquarists think they are one and the same, but the scientific evidence is not yet available for such a conclusion to be warranted. Photo by H. Hansen.

Cichlasoma aureum is a member of the *Thorichthys* group. Native to British Honduras, it is now being propagated in Florida fish ponds for eventual distribution to aquarists. Photo by Dr. R. J. Goldstein.

Cichlasoma hellebrunni, the chocolate cichlid. Large adult. Photo by Dr. R. J. Goldstein.

Juveniles of one of the species of *Cichlasoma*, possibly *C. hellebrunni* or *C. coryphaenoides*. Photo by Harald Schultz.

SUMMARY OF SPECIES OF THE GENUS *CICHLASOMA* SWAINSON*

aceroides
adspersum
affine
alfaroi
altifrons
arnoldi
atromaculatum
aureum
autochthon
balteatum[1]
bartoni
beani
bifasciatum
bimaculatum
bocourti
bulleri
callolepis
calobrense
centrarchus
champotonis
citrinellum[2]
coryphaenoides[3]
cyanoguttatum
dowi (syn: *dovii*)
eigenmanni
ellioti[4]
erythraeum[2]
facetum
fenestratum
festae
festivum
friedrichsthalii[5]
gadowi
geddesi
godmani
guttulatum (syn: *zonatum*)
hellebrunni[3]
helleri[4]
heterospilum
hogaboomorum
hyorhynchum
immaculatum
intermedium
irregulare
istlanum
kraussii
labiatum[2]
labridens
lentiginosum
lobochilus
longimanus
lyonsi
macracanthum (syn: *heterodontum*)
maculicauda
managuense
margaritiferum
meeki
melanurum
mento
microphthalmum (syns: *oblongum, milleri, caeruleogula*)
motaguense[5]
myersi
nebuliferum
nicaraguense[1]
nigrofasciatum
oblongum

* Sets of numbered superscripts (e.g., *helleri*[4] and *ellioti*[4]) indicate that the two or more nomina (names) may apply to fewer or to a single species.

octofasciatum (syn: *hedricki*)
ornatum
pasionis
pavonaceum
pearsei
popenoei
psitticum
ramsdeni
robertsoni (syn: *acutum*)
rostratum
salvini
severum
sexfasciatum
sieboldi (syns: *Herichthys underwoodi, Paraneetroplus sieboldi*)
spectabile
spilotum
spilurum (syn: *cutteri*)
spinosissimum
steindachneri
synspilum (syn: *hicklingi*)
temporale (syn: *crassa*)
tenue
terrabae
tetracanthus (syn: *haitiensis*)
trimaculatum (syns: *mojarra, centrale, gordonsmithi, cajali*)
tuba (syn: *Tomocichla underwoodi*)
tuyrense
umbriferum
urophthalmus

One final word on *Cichlasoma*. The type species of the genus is *C. bimaculatum*. This fish is very close in many characters to *Aequidens portalegrensis*. It is in this close relationship that the stability of *Cichlasoma* is on thin ice. We should not be surprised to see a complete revision of these two, and related, genera in the not-too-distant future. I know of nobody who is currently doing this, but the problem seems to be well-recognized in the ichthyological community.

THE GENUS *PETENIA*

Petenia Günther, 1862 is monotypic, i.e., it contains only a single species, *P. splendida* Günther, 1862. It occurs in southeastern Mexico, northern Guatemala and British Honduras (Usumacinta Province). This is a large, predaceous fish, rather elongate and generally rather gray with dark blotches on the flanks. Juveniles are very thin-bodied, which emphasizes the large mouth and reminds one almost of a leaf fish. Erythric (red) individuals have been taken recently in British Honduras. One observer noted that, of three spawning pairs, the female in every case was the red

Cichlasoma cyanoguttatum, the Texas cichlid, guarding eggs. Bob Ozibko of California has crossed the Texas cichlid with the firemouth *(C. meeki)* to produce a fish called the firetex. He then crossed a firetex with *C. nigrofasciatum!* Photo by Stanislav Frank.

Cichlasoma erythraeum, *C. citrinellum* and *C. labiatum* may actually be only one or two species, and ideas proliferate faster than good data. Members of this group *may* go through yellow and white phases before turning red, and may never turn red. Several develop big fleshy lips with age. Photo by Mervin F. Roberts.

Chuco axelrodi from the Orinoco basin becomes black as an adult, but is dull brown as a juvenile (below). Not yet available in the hobby but its locality will not be difficult to reach. Photos by Dr. Herbert R. Axelrod.

fish while the male was normally pigmented. The red form is known locally as the red snook. *P. splendida* is able to open its mouth in telescopic fashion, much like *Cichlasoma kraussii* (see below). I am grateful to Bob Rawlins of Beldt's Aquarium (Hazelwood, Missouri) for a specimen of the red snook, for parasitological examination.

At one time three other species were included in the nominal genus *Petenia; myersi, spectabile* and *kraussii*. It is now believed that they properly belong in *Cichlasoma,* group *Parapetenia.*

THE GENUS *CHUCO*

The genus *Chuco* Fernandez-Yepez, 1969 was established to contain a small number of fishes of the *Cichlasoma* line of evolution (more than three anal spines) that contained the following set of characteristics: the penultimate dorsal spine is longer than the third dorsal spine; the branchial arch contains no upper lobe; the preoperculum is entire; intermaxillary process equal to or shorter than the snout length; pectoral fins extending to the origin of the anal fin; anal fin with four or more spines; dorsal fin with thirteen or more spines; teeth conical in a single row, with some teeth in patches on the upper jaw and lower jaw bones; soft parts of dorsal and anal fin partially scaled.

The species in this genus are: *C. milleri* (Meek, 1907), *C. manana* Fernandez-Yepez, 1969, and *C. axelrodi* Fernandez-Yepez, 1971. Both *C. manana* and *C. milleri* are found north of the Isthmus of Panama, while *C. axelrodi* is found in northern South America in the Orinoco basin. See the photographs for the coloration of this last species. As an adult this fish is blackish and quite attractive, but apparently it will be a while before living specimens are imported for propagation.

POSTSCRIPT

For recent papers on the distribution of neotropical cichlids, see Riedel (1972), Gilbert and Kelso (1971), and Ovchynnyk (1971).

11

Cichlids of Africa

The majority of the world's cichlids are native to Africa, with the preponderance of species occurring in the Great Lakes of the eastern part of the continent. I will present the African cichlids by genus for the western and southern groups, and by lake for the fishes of the major lakes. The island fauna of Madagascar is presented separately.

The major features of the African land mass are the extensive river systems of the central and western part of the continent, including the Congo, Niger and many smaller streams, all draining into the Atlantic from deep inside the continent; and the Great Lakes of east Africa, with associated (but not necessarily connected) rivers, including the Ruzizi, Zambezi, and Limpopo drainages. The Limpopo and Zambezi flow eastward and empty into the Indian Ocean. At the northern end of the continent is the Nile delta, and its river extends well southward into the African continent where it terminates (or arises) in the vicinity of Lakes Albert and Victoria. There are many huge lakes in this area, which pale in comparison with the Great Lakes. Thus, the picture presented herein is only an abstract of the whole story, and we have a great deal more to learn.

The principal African cichlid genera are *Tilapia, Haplochromis* and *Lamprologus,* but many more will be handled individually. The taxonomy of the African cichlids has undergone greater flux than the taxonomy of neotropical genera and species. Information of many genera of interest is fuzzy at best, totally unavailable at worst. Africa is only being lightly tapped at present, and it will be decades before aquarists have even an inkling of the true situation and the vast variation to be found in the cichlids. Photography and preservation of species, with good locality data, will be essential if we hope to avoid a total morass. Fortunately,

Haplochromis fenestratus, recently imported from Lake Malawi. Photo by Dr. Robert J. Goldstein.

Limnochromis otostigma of Lake Tanganyika has a head profile much like species of *Xenotilapia*. However, the black "ear" is more prominent in members of the former genus. Photo by Homer Arment.

This is one of the myriad types of collecting sites in Africa. Besides the lakes, streams such as this one produce many species of interest to the hobbyist. Photo by Dr. Herbert R. Axelrod.

Brichard at Lake Tanganyika is doing a good job of identifications, unlike the mess that was imported from others at Lake Malawi.

THE GENUS *TILAPIA*

The genus *Tilapia* Smith, 1840 is presently considered to contain about eighty described species, divided into a number of subgenera and other groups without names of taxonomic status. It is likely that some of the subgenera will be raised to generic rank, thus reducing the number of nominal species within this very large genus. Notice that 1840 was a very good year for ichthyology, for not only was this vast African group first defined but the famous work of Heckel on the American cichlids appeared at the same time. The species of the divisions of *Tilapia* are presented in the table.

The usual mode of reproduction in *Tilapia* is maternal mouthbrooding, but other types of brooding behavior are known. These will be discussed later, with a review of behavioral papers.

Only a few of the species are known in the hobby, and most of these are of limited attractiveness. However, there are many very beautiful species known to African workers. In general, species of *Tilapia* occur in rivers, but many occur in lakes; the group is primarily, however, fluviatile (riverine). Most species are not predaceous in habit, but feed on plankton or vegetation. In aquaria they are omnivorous, but should have some plant material in the diet, and a largely herbivorous diet is preferred. Because of their rapid growth and heavy feeding upon plants and plankton, a number of species have been seeded in fish ponds around the world as a source of cheap protein, and their transplanting into rice paddies is well-known. There is a tendency, however, for these fishes to rapidly overpopulate a pond in the absence of predators. This results in stunted fish, which are of lowered value as food. Stunting is often associated with early breeding age in this genus, and the problem of overpopulation is the single most important problem to African fisheries personnel. The use of sterile hybrids has to a great extent alleviated the problem.

Species of *Tilapia* have a distribution practically throughout Africa and parts of the Arabian peninsula. They occur in rivers that drain into the Atlantic, and in the Great Rift lakes of East

Africa. They occur northward into the Nile delta, and southward to South Africa. Their absence anywhere would be cause for surprise. They have been introduced onto the island of Madagascar, and have even been introduced into some waters of the United States, resulting in a recent article in a sport-fishing magazine lauding this new panfish! See Lachner *et al.* (1970) for details of U.S. distribution.

The pharyngeal structure of *Tilapia* is the basis of a fundamental division in cichlid taxonomy. In *Tilapia* the parasphenoid bones of the palate are fused with the skull in the formation of the apophysis. In the *Haplochromis* line of evolution another bone, the basioccipital, is also involved in the fusion. (See also the introduction to the American cichlids.) Because of this basic division in cichlids, a number of genera are allied to *Tilapia,* which becomes a fundamentally important genus to ichthyologists as well as to the people who eat them. The definition of *Tilapia* is still in a state of flux, as some of its subgroups may be taken out and given generic status.

Tilapia melanotheron, the blackchin mouthbrooder, was at one time very popular in the hobby. Today it is rarely seen. Photo by Laurence E. Perkins, F.Z.S.

Tilapia tholloni. Photo courtesy of the American Museum of Natural History.

Tilapia guineensis. Photo by D. Terver of the Nancy Aquarium, France.

Tilapia buettikoferi. Photo by E. Roloff.

Tilapia aurea. You can catch all you want in the canals of southern Florida. Photo by Klaus Paysan.

A number of species names used in the hobby continue to undergo changes, either because they were originally incorrectly applied or because some names have become junior synonyms of other names. For example, *melanopleura* is now replaced by *rendalli;* the blackchin mouthbrooder is now known as *melanotheron*, rather than *macrocephala* or *heudelotii*. See the table for the breakdown of the genus; the table is based on Thys (1968).

PRESENT DISPOSITION OF THE GENUS *TILAPIA*

Genus *Tilapia* Smith, 1840

Subgenus *Tilapia* Smith, 1840

T.(T.) sparrmanii Smith, 1840

T.(T.) ruweti Poll & Thys, 1965

Subgenus *Trewavasia* Thys, 1968

T.(T.) guinasana Trewavas, 1936

Subgenus *Pelmatolapia* Thys, 1968

T.(P.) mariae Boul., 1899

T.(P.) eisentrauti Trewavas, 1962

T.(P.) cabrae Boul., 1898

T.(P.) bilinata Pellegrin, 1900

T.(P.) brevimanus Boul., 1912

Subgenus *Pelmatochromis* Steindachner, 1895

T.(P.) busumana (Günther, 1902)

[1]*T.(P.) buettikoferi* Steindachner, 1895

T.(P.) ocellifer Boul., 1899

[1]*T.(P.) congicus* Boul., 1897

Subgenus *Heterotilapia* Regan, 1920

[1]*T.(H.) buttikoferi* (Hubrecht, 1883)

T. (H.) cessiana Thys, 1968

Subgenus *Coptodon* Gervais, 1853

T.(C.) zillii (Gervais, 1848)

T.(C.) guineensis (Bleeker, 1862)

T.(C.) walteri Thys, 1968

T.(C.) cameronensis Holly, 1927

[2]*T.(C.) nyongana* Thys, 1968

[1]*T.(C.) congica* Poll & Thys, 1960

T.(C.) rendalli (Boul., 1896) (includes two subspp.: *swierstrae, gefuensis*)

T.(C.) discolor (Günther, 1902)

T.(C.) kottae Lonnberg, 1904

T.(C.) deckerti Thys, 1967

T.(C.) tholloni (Sauvage, 1884)

T.(C.) margaritacea Boul., 1916

[2]*T.(C.) louka* Thys, 1969

Subgenus *Dagetia* Thys, 1968

T.(D.) rheophila Daget, 1962

Subgenus *Danakilia* Thys, 1968

T.(D.) franchettii Vinciguerra, 1932

Subgenus *Neotilapia* Regan, 1920

T.(N.) tanganicae (Günther, 1893)

T.(N.) karomo Poll, 1948

Subgenus *Alcolapia* Thys, 1968

T.(A.) grahami Boul., 1912

T.(A.) alcalica Hilgendorf, 1905

T.(A.) amphimelas Hilgendorf, 1905

Subgenus *Nyasalapia* Thys, 1968

T.(N.) squamipinnis (Günther, 1864)

T.(N.) karongae Trewavas, 1941

T.(N.) sake Lowe, 1952

T.(N.) lidole Trewavas, 1941

Subgenus *Loruwiala* Thys, 1968

T.(L.) variabilis Boul., 1906

T.(L.) upembae Thys, 1964

T.(L.) rukwaensis Hilg. & Pappenheim, 1903

T.(L.) macrochir Boul., 1912

T.(L.) salinicola Poll, 1948

[2]*T.(L.) angolensis* Trewavas

T.(L.) lepidura Boul., 1899

T.(L.) schwebischi (Sauvage, 1884)

Subgenus *Oreochromis* Günther, 1894

T.(O.) nigra (Günther, 1894) (subspp.: *nigra, spilurus)*

T.(O.) percivali Boul., 1912

T.(O.) korogwe Lowe, 1955

T.(O.) hornorum Trewavas, 1966

T.(O.) urolepis Norman, 1922

T.(O.) mossambica (Peters, 1852)
T.(O.) mortimeri Trewavas, 1966
T.(O.) andersonii (De Castelnau, 1866)
T.(O.) hunteri (Günther, 1899)
T.(O.) girigan Lowe, 1955
T.(O.) jipe Lowe, 1955
T.(O.) pangani Lowe, 1955
T.(O.) ruvumae Trewavas, 1966
T.(O.) shirana (Boul., 1896) (subspp.: *shirana, chilwae)*
T.(O.) placida Trewavas, 1941
GROUP III-G
T. aurea (Steindachner, 1864) (subspp.: *aurea, exul)*
T. leucosticta Trewavas, 1933
T. esculenta Graham, 1928
GROUP III-H
T. nilotica (Hasselquist, 1757) (subspp.: *nilotica, eduardiana, cancellata)*
Subgenus *Sarotherodon* Ruppell, 1854
T.(S.) heudelotii Dumeril, 1859
T.(S.) melanotheron (Ruppell, 1854)
T.(S.) nigripinnis Guichenot, 1859
T.(S.?) lohbergeri Holly, 1930
T.(S.?) linnellii Lonnberg, 1904
T.(S.?) mvogoi Thys, 1965
GROUP III-J (possibly to be included in *Sarotherodon).*
T.(S.?) galilaea (Artedi, 1757) (subspp.: *galilaea, borkuana, pleuromelas, multifasciata, boulengeri)*
T.(S.?) occidentalis Daget, 1962
T.(S.?) sanagaensis Thys, 1966
T.(S.?) steinbachi Trewavas, 1962
T.(S.?) tournieri Daget, 1965
T.(S.?) caudomarginata Boul., 1916

EXPLANATION OF COMMENTS:
[1] Because of the similarity in spelling, and as a result of having *Pelmatochromis* brought within *Tilapia* as a subgenus, it seems that these names will not stand unless in some way modified, e.g., as "*P.-congicum.*" In any case, it will probably be Thys who decides the best way to treat this new nomenclatural problem: whether to use only the oldest synonym and change the nomen (name) of the subsequently described taxon (natural group), or to add a letter as a modifier to the name.
[2] These names were *nomina nuda* (names without descriptions) at the time of publication but may well be valid at present.

At least six species are known to be typical substratum brooders. These are *Tilapia sparrmanii* (usually greenish, with a hint of red on its shoulder, but black when brooding), *T. mariae, T. rendalli, T. zillii, T. tholloni,* and *T. guinasana.*

Tilapia sparrmanii at one time was quite popular in the hobby, but it is only seen on occasion today. In the past year a number of imports of this species have appeared, but aquarists had difficulty recognizing the fish, most of which were juveniles. The overall coloration is silvery green, and the male tends to have a slight red flush to its shoulder region. In nature the eggs tend to be green, and this probably reflects the rich vegetational diet.

Tilapia leucosticta. One of the endemic cichlids of Lake Victoria. Photo by Hilmar Hansen.

Tilapia sparrmanii, a nesting species in a genus of mouthbrooders. Brooding males turn almost black, with or without the reddish shoulder patch. Photo by Dr. Robert J. Goldstein.

Tilapia mossambica, female above, nuptial male below. Upper photo by Dr. Herbert R. Axelrod; lower photo by Klaus Paysan.

Breeding occurs at about two and a half inches, and the fish does not attain very large size. Parents guard their young vigorously, and tend to blackness. A very easy fish to breed.

Tilapia mariae is one of the newer fishes in the hobby, having been introduced to American aquarists only a few years ago. This fish was originally described as two separate species, for the juveniles have a pattern of vertical bands while the adults have only a series of about six or seven lateral spots, and a slightly different profile. This is a large fish, and seven-inch specimens are probably common by now. They breed at about three and a half inches and, except at this time, are very peaceful for substratum brooders. Recently Bill Fisher of Oklahoma City found a few black-tailed sports in one spawning, proceeded to breed for this character, and subsequently distributed black-tailed *T. mariae* all over the country.

Tilapia tholloni is a large fish, silvery overall, with a red breast. Breeding occurs at about five or six inches, and the fry are good live food for other fishes (and that's about all you can do with them!). *T. rendalli* also has a red breast and is otherwise rather similar, except for a tendency to banding on the upper flanks.

Tilapia tholloni.

Tilapia galilaea is intermediate between the typical substratum brooders just discussed and the typical mouthbrooders. It occupies the same position in *Tilapia* that *Geophagus jurupari* occupies in its American genus, with some important differences. *T. galilaea* is widely distributed in northeast Africa. A long-term pair bond of perhaps two weeks duration precedes courtship and spawning. Spawning is characterized by the depositing of a mass of sticky eggs. At the completion of spawning, after a lapse of ten to fifteen minutes, the eggs are picked up for oral incubation. In the northern part of its range, the male usually begins picking up the eggs, although both parents often take care of incubation. Farther south, it is usually thc female that initiates egg pickup, but again, either or both parents are involved in the incubation.

Most species of *Tilapia* are total mouthbrooders, and generally they are maternal brooders. Biparental and paternal brooders are also well known. In the case of maternal brooders, the male is often richly and differently colored from the female, defines and guards a spawning territory, accepts females into his territory for purposes of spawning, forms a very brief pair bond with her, spawns, and drives her away. She will then usually travel to a region remote from the spawning grounds for incubation and eventual release of the fry. In the cases of paternal or biparental brooding the differences between the sexes are markedly reduced or totally obliterated from the point of view of the aquarist.

The best known paternal brooder is the blackchin mouthbrooder, *Tilapia melanotheron* (previously known in the hobby as *macrocephala* or *heudelotii*). The behavior of this fish has been well documented by Barlow and Green (1969, 1970). The blackchin mouthbrooder does not illustrate any great differences between the sexes, nor does behavior of the male and female in courtship differ much either. Generally, one will find a successful spawning if the male is somewhat smaller than the female. But whatever the size relationship between the sexes, it is the smaller fish that seems to court more. Blackchins go through the usual fighting-preceding-courtship of other cichlids, but it is mostly eyewash and damage to either partner is relatively rare.

Sometimes, two females will spawn, thus emphasizing that courtship maneuvers of the two sexes hardly differ preceding spawning. About the only sexual difference to be seen is in the

Tilapia mariae adult with very young fry. Photo by G. Marcuse.

The young have reached the age of eight weeks and now show the typical color pattern of the juvenile *Tilapia mariae*. Photo by G. Marcuse.

Tilapia mariae, juvenile above, adult below. A blackish-tailed strain, developed by Bill Fisher of Oklahoma City, is now available.

color of the opercular spot; in the female it is red and in the male it is yellow. There is an unusually long courtship period in this species (compared to other kinds of mouthbrooders). It probably allows for the male to prepare for his long fasting period during buccal incubation. Thus, it is the male that must be physiologically ready for the rigors of incubation without food; a period of ten to fourteen days of incubation is involved. The sex roles are not reversed; they are simply not as sharply distinct from one another.

For studies on *Tilapia guineensis*, *T. mariae* (a typical substratum brooder), *T. macrochir*, and the intermediate *T. galilaea*, see Apfelbach (1970) and Apfelbach and Leong (1970). For studies and hypotheses concerning the origins of mouthbrooding in *Tilapia* see Lowe-McConnell (1959), Ruwet (1968) and for data on other species see Trewavas (1966), and Fishelson (1967).

Thys (1970) was particularly concerned with the origins of mouthbrooding behavior in the subgenus *Coptodon*, but went into considerable detail in discussing other sections of the genus. He noted that the paternal mouthbrooder *T.* (*C.*) *discolor* differs from the paternal mouthbrooder *T. melanotheron* in that the male of the former is typically much larger than the female, but the reasons for this remain unknown. Thys feels that mouthbrooding arose independently at least four times within the genus *Tilapia*, and also independently in *Tylochromis*, *Chromidotilapia*, and *Haplochromis*. (*Tylochromis* species are apparently maternal brooders, as are species of *Haplochromis;* species of *Chromidotilapia* are paternal or biparental.) Although substratum spawning is (of course) ancestral to mouthbrooding, it is probably the pit spawners (rather than hard substratum-spawners) that are ancestral to mouthbrooders. For, it is clear, pit spawners tend to produce eggs of reduced stickiness, and this is usually necessary for oral incubation which is, apparently, a method for providing current around the eggs and washing them of metabolites. Maternal, paternal or biparental mouthbrooding could have arisen directly from pit spawning, and it is not necessary to hypothesize intermediate stages or any sequence of different parental brooding roles; however, such stages are not ruled out in the history of particular groups.

In the maternal brooders it is usually the male which is colorful and territorial, and this is seen in the common Mozambique mouthbrooder, *Tilapia mossambica*, a very common fish in the hobby. Males tend to become black, with red edging to the tail fin. Females remain pale. There is only a brief period of courtship, followed by spawning (often under community conditions), and the female is then either driven away aggressively or leaves to avoid further sexual advances. A new golden red sport of this species appeared in the hobby in 1971, and rivals the Rift Lake cichlids for beauty. It was developed by Hillard Marcus of Aquarium Stock Company in Los Angeles, California.

The eggs of mouthbrooders are larger than those of substratum types, and tend to have thinner shells and a lack of sticky structures. This reduced egg membrane system was studied by Dadzie (1968). The development of the embryos was studied in great depth by Fishelson (1966).

The same author (Fishelson, 1967) later studied the behavior of fry. The fry of *Tilapia* species orient toward each other via the dark ocellus found in practically all juveniles (located on the

Tilapia galilaea has an unusual type of egg incubation. About fifteen minutes after spawning is completed, the whole mass of eggs is picked up, by one or by both parents. Photo by G. Marcuse.

Tilapia (Sarotherodon) heudelotii is a difficult fish to identify, and for this reason strains of *Tilapia* should be carefully catalogued before releasing them to the aquarium public. Photo by Klaus Paysan.

This is an unidentified species of *Stomatepia* from Barombi-ma-Mbu, a crater lake in Cameroon. Photo by Dr. R. J. Goldstein.

Tilapia shirana of Lake Malawi. Photo by Michael Oliver.

Tilapia guineensis, like *Tilapia tholloni,* is a red-breasted substratum nester. The former species is illustrated here. It attains large size, and is not unusual in the hobby. Photo by Dr. R. J. Goldstein.

dorsal fin) of this genus. Earlier in life they orient toward any dark area, such as the mother's mouth, gill opening, etc. He managed to have a group of them follow a ball with a hole in it, repeatedly trying to enter the hole.

Although largely fluviatile, species of *Tilapia* are also found in lakes, and a sampling would include the following:

Lake	All Tilapia	Endemic Tilapia
Rudolf	3	0
Albert	4	0
Tanganyika	4	2
Edward	2	0
Victoria	2	2
Malawi	6	5
Rukwa	1	1
Jipe	2	2

These data may no longer be valid, as fisheries personnel are often engaged in transplanting species of *Tilapia* as a food source in areas where a successful introduction is considered likely. Such areas would include a good source of vegetation or plankton not presently being fully exploited.

Tilapia contains many species of realized or potential value to the hobby, but they tend to overproduce. Thus, disposal of fry is always a problem. Practically all juveniles look alike, and are rather drab and silvery with the *Tilapia* spot on the dorsal fin. The fry are excellent food for piscivorous fishes and, in the absence of other living foods, should be so used.

Additional references to work on species of *Tilapia* are the following: Hyder (1969, 1970a, 1970b) and Eckstein and Katz (1971) on gonadal physiology; Badawi and Said (1971) on blood values; Lanzing (1971) on effects of anaesthetics; Stevens and Fry (1970) on temperature adjustments; Aronson (1948) on *T. melanotheron* (for comparison with more recent works by Barlow and Green); Trewavas (1966) on *T. aurea* and others; Whitehead (1966) for *T. mariae*; Iles and Holden (1969) for *T. galilaea;* Chervinski (1968a, 1968b) for *T. zillii* and *T. aurea;* Poll and Thys (1960) for *T. tholloni congica;* Privat (1970) for *T. rendalli;* Thys (1968) for a comprehensive bibliography of the entire genus; and the following regionally important papers: Robinson and Robinson

(1971) on the food sources of Lake Chad; Fagade (1971) for the Lagos Lagoon; and Fishelson (1967) for the species in Israel; also see Fryer and Iles (1969) for thoughts on the evolution of species of *Tilapia* in the African lakes.

THE CONGO RIVER SYSTEM

Below the hump of Africa the equator cuts through the continent. To the west it occurs between Cape Lopez and Rio Muni, passing through Gabon, into the Congo, passing through Uganda, the northern tip of Lake Victoria, into Kenya and out into the Indian Ocean. Along the path of the equator are two important water systems, Lake Victoria in East Africa and the Congo River system, occupying the entire western half of equatorial Africa.

The Congo System is massive, containing many tributaries of diverse names, and as an introduction I will try to simplify the general pattern. Picture the Congo System as a massive tree, with its base on the west coast at the juncture of three nations. In the center is a small strip of The Congo on the coast. To the north is Gabon and to the south is Angola. The base of the Congo River empties into the Atlantic within the narrow strip of The Congo (formerly the Belgian Congo). The shape of the main stream as it courses inland and upriver is northeastward, where it levels out near the center of the continent, and begins to course southeastward toward Stanleyville. Just to the southeast of this city occur the Stanley Falls, and above the falls the main stream is known as the Lualaba River. Tributaries of the Lualaba extend toward the east coming close to Lake Kivu and Lake Tanganyika in the Great Rift Valley of East Africa. A very distant tributary of the Lualaba, known as the Luvua River, reaches southward and to the west of southern Lake Tanganyika where it reaches Lake Mweru.

So far we have talked of the main stream of the Congo River, but there are big tributaries as well. The major northern tributary running between The Congo and Gabon is the Ubangi River (spelled various ways). It divides the old Belgian Congo from the old French Equatorial Africa. The major southern stream is the Kasai River reaching southward through the lower part of The Congo, and its tributaries extend largely straight southward into northern Angola. Because of the myriad tributaries on each of these major streams, and the variation in names (and name spelling) for all these rivers, there has been much taxonomic confusion over the years as to where a particular species originated. For our purposes, it will suffice to treat this entire drainage system as a unit, for to indicate which species occur in which streams (and then to identify the location of each of these streams) would be extremely tedious. As the main stream of the Congo River passes on both sides of the Equator, and the Kasai runs south of the equator while the Ubangi runs north of it, it is clear that the entire drainage system may be considered generally equatorial.

Poll (1967) reviewed much of the Kasai River fauna in his monumental *Contribution a la faune ichthyologique de l'Angola.* The southern part of Angola is drained by still another major river system, the Zambezi River. And yet there are still other important river systems involved. He found many species of fishes in several of these systems, but I will only indicate Congo occurrence in this section to avoid loading the reader with too much material.

Chromidotilapia species, possibly *C. guentheri.*

Chromidotilapia guentheri, adult above, juvenile below. Upper photo by Ruda Zukal; lower photo by Hilmar Hansen.

A number of species of *Tilapia* occur in these waters, including *cabrae, lepidura, macrochir, rendalli, schwebischi, sparrmanii,* and *ruweti*; there is some question as to *galilaea* and *zillii*. Note that *ruweti* was previously placed in *Pelmatochromis,* but Thys has since revised that group. *Hemichromis fasciatus* occurs in the Congo drainage of Angola also, but it is widespread through central and west Africa. Several species of *Serranochromis* occur in these waters, including: *angusticeps, macrocephalus, robustus,* and *thumbergi*. These also are widespread fishes occurring in other rivers, and none of the group is restricted to the Congo Basin. A large cichlid genus, as expected, is *Haplochromis,* here represented by *mellandi, thysi,* and *welwitschii*; several other species occur in the nearby river systems.

Vast areas of the Congo share many similar or identical forms, but our knowledge is based largely on fishes of a large lake called the Stanley Pool, located near the mouth of the river at Leopoldville (Kinshasa). Included are species of *Nanochromis, Leptotilapia* (formerly *Gobiochromis*) and the widely distributed *Lamprologus,* the latter explosively speciating in Lake Tanganyika. *Leptotilapia* has a number of similarities to *Steatocranus*. Still another genus is *Teleogramma*, wormlike fishes of substratum brooding habits.

THE CUNENE RIVER AND THE GAMBIA RIVER

The Cunene River empties into the Atlantic at about 17.5°S, well below the mouth of the Congo River, and at the southern border of Angola. Poll (1967) listed the following cichlids from this basin: *Tilapia andersonii, T. galilaea* (questionable report), *T. rendalli, T. sparrmanii,* and possibly *T. steindachneri; Serranochromis angusticeps, S. macrocephalus,* and *S. thumbergi; Haplochromis acuticeps, H. angolensis, H. darlingi, H. frederici, H. machadoi, H. mellandi,* and *Hemihaplochromis philander*. Known from the Cunene River is *Sargochromis angolensis*. The genera, where appropriate, are dealt with separately. Also see Jubb (1967).

The Gambia River has the westernmost drainage of all the rivers of Africa, emptying at about 17°W, 13°N. The fishes of this river ought to tell us something of the western limits of certain genera, and indeed they were studied by Svensson (1933) in depth. A common fish here is *Hemichromis fasciatus* type A. "*Hemichromis*" *bimaculatus* is also common in these waters. As expected, one also finds the widespread *Tilapia galilaea*. Svensson reported *T. melanopleura* here also, but that name has been replaced by *T. rendalli*. Long before Svensson, another worker reported the presence of "*Pelmatochromis jentinki* (Steindachner)," but Svensson found none himself. This fish is now known as *Tylochromis jentinki*. Paul Loiselle (pers. comm.) reports *Tilapia (P.) buettikoferi* in the Gambia basin.

THE GENUS *CHROMIDOTILAPIA*

The genus *Chromidotilapia* (Thys, 1968) contains a number of species formerly placed in either *Tilapia* or the old genus *Pelmatochromis*. Characteristics of this group include a well-developed hanging pad on the roof of the pharynx, tuberculate and broad gillrakers on the first gill arch with all of them about equal in size, the lack of prolongations on the caudal fin, the lack of microgillrakers, and pelvic fins the same in both sexes (pointed, and with the outer rays longest). Seven species are presently included in this genus, not all of them named. These will be discussed individually, but it is probable that they are mostly paternal or biparental mouthbrooders. The species include:

C. guentheri (Sauvage, 1882)
C. kingsleyae (Boulenger, 1898)
C. batesii (Boulenger, 1901)
C. loennbergi (Trewavas, 1962)
C. schoutedeni (Poll and Thys, 1967)
C. exsul (Trewavas, 1933)—invalid (see below)
"Shiloango-species" to be named shortly.

The best-known species is *C. guentheri*, native to Ivory Coast, Sierra Leone, Liberia, Nigeria, Ghana, Dahomey and Cameroon, i.e., Mid-Atlantic Africa. Widely distributed in forested habitats. This species is well known to aquarists as a paternal mouthbrooder. Breeding behavior was described in depth by Myrberg (1965). Courtship and spawning resemble the situations in other cichlid substratum brooders, but at the end of spawning the male picks up the eggs for nine to twelve days of incubation.

At the end of this time the free-swimming young are released, but picked up at night or in times of danger. This post-release pickup may continue as long as ten to twelve days, but after this time they are too large to get back in the adults' mouths. Although only the male incubates the eggs and fry, both parents may pick up the fry afterward. The pair remains together post-spawning and during the next eight weeks. Loiselle (1971) reports that apparently two distinct species occur in nature, and ichthyologists have been using the same name for both, thinking that there was only the one. This same author presented a comprehensive life color description of *C. guentheri* and a review of breeding. The male picks up the eggs *as they are spawned,* and may occasionally spit them out and pick them back up again, apparently in an attempt to fit them in his buccal pouch properly. Loiselle's other observations agree with Myrberg's.

Thysia ansorgii. Photo by Wolfgang Bechtle.

Thysia ansorgii. Photo by Ruda Zukal.

Thysia ansorgii, male. Photo by Ruda Zukal.

Chromidotilapia batesii also, according to Thys (1968), consists of two species in nature, occurring in Rio Muni and vicinity, and on the island of Fernando Po. According to Scheel (pers. communication) these two forms are quite similar when preserved, but quite differently colored when alive. The northern form picks up the eggs for mouthbrooding at once, while the southern form waits about 24 hours before picking them up for mouthbrooding. The southern form has blood red colors near the top of the caudal fin. In fact, according to Scheel, ". . . the southern (*C.*) *batesii* is a beauty." Scheel has distributed this fish among Copenhagen aquarists, and hopefully northern and southern forms will find their way into the tanks of American aquarists shortly. The ranges of both species overlap, but the fishes do not interbreed in nature.

Chromidotilapia loennbergi is known only from Lake Barombi-ba-Kotto, a crater lake, and from Lake Mboandong which is connected to the other lake. This western Cameroon species resemble *C. guentheri* in colors, but *C. batesii* in body shape. Another species of the genus is *C. kingsleyae* from lower Gabon, characterized by a long snout profile, silvery white flanks with blue-black side markings, and a red outer margin to the caudal and dorsal fins. Female colors not reported. A mouthbrooder, but the details are unknown.

C. schoutedeni occurs in the Congo drainage, and is sexually dichromatic and dimorphic. Brooding information not known, but Thys generally considers the genus to be biparental or paternal mouthbrooders.

C. exsul is poorly known, and occurs in Lake Rudolf. Loiselle (pers. comm.) has studied the type specimens in the British Museum, and considers them to be juveniles of "*Hemichromis*" *bimaculatus*.

The Shiloango species may actually be a mixture of species, due to its broad and discontinuous distribution in vast reaches of the Congo. It apparently has been confused with other named species in the scientific literature, and it will be some time until Thys clears up the confusion. It (or they) resemble both *C. batesii* and *C. schoutedeni*, rather than *C. guentheri*. Apparently Brichard's Congo station has access to this fish (or one of its forms), and aquarists should be careful to keep any unusual imports separate from established aquarium stocks.

Chromidotilapia guentheri, male butting female. Photo by Ruda Zukal.

THE GENUS *THYSIA*

During the past decade, with the great influx of African imports, a number of cichlids became available to scientists as well as to aquarists, leading to some basic changes in ichthyological nomenclature. The genus *Thysia* Loiselle and Welcomme, 1972 provides a case in point. The type species (on which the genus is based) is *T. ansorgii* (Boulenger, 1901), previously known in the hobby as *Pelmatochromis ansorgii*. It had been thought (Thys, 1968) that *ansorgii* was the same fish known as *arnoldi* and *annectens*. However, Loiselle and Welcomme believe that *Thysia annectens* should be relegated to the status of a *species inquirenda*, which means that it is in limbo pending further study. The fish known as *arnoldi* is indeed the same as *ansorgii*, but *ansorgii* is the older and thereby valid name. An additional species, discovered by Tyson Roberts, and not yet described and named, appears to be related to *Thysia*. The genus *Thysia* seems to be rather generalized, and related to the genus *Hemichromis*, rather than to the *Nanochromis-Pelvicachromis-Chromidotilapia* line of evolution.

"Pelmatochromis" thomasi, spawning sequence. Photos by H. J. Richter.

Hemichromis bimaculatus, the jewel cichlid.

Thysia ansorgii is a very peaceful substratum brooder, and can be recognized by several characters. First, it is light colored, with a series of dark blotches on the side. Females are characterized by a few to very many black spots in the lower part of the dorsal fin membrane. Males are characterized by an asymmetrical caudal fin, the upper lobe considerably longer than the lower. In both, but usually in the male, the upper part of the caudal fin is margined with red and white. There is little prenuptial activity, the fish is not at all aggressive, and they are not the most reliable of parents. Artificial incubation of the eggs is recommended. For a breeding report see Zukal (1971).

Another species, apparently related to *T. ansorgii*, was previously called *Pelmatochromis cerasogaster* (Boulenger, 1899). Whether it will go into the new genus for *ansorgii* and *annectens* is unknown at present. But it will have to go somewhere, for *Pelmatochromis* in its present position (taxonomically) is a subgenus of *Tilapia*, and this fish is probably not a member of that genus.

THE *THOMASI-BIMACULATUS* GROUP

When Thys reappraised the old genus *Pelmatochromis*, a number of problems arose. For example, *Pelmatochromis thomasi* (Boulenger, 1916) appeared to be more closely related to *Hemichromis bimaculatus* (Gill, 1862) than to anything else. These two species will shortly be united by Thys into a new genus, but as this has not yet been published I am unable to provide the name. When it appears, readers are advised to re-head this section with the name of the new genus, which will be reported to the hobby in my column in *Tropical Fish Hobbyist* magazine.

The spawning behavior of both species is well known. They are typical substratum brooders, but only *bimaculatus* is well-known to American aquarists. Adults tend to orange or green, and in some strains this is a sexual difference. A recent importation (during 1971) consisted of reddish fish with many longitudinal rows of iridescent scales. The jewel fish (*bimaculatus*) is an excellent parent, but a belligerent fish, and not recommended for even a cichlid community tank. The fry can always find a market, and this species is therefore recommended for the cichlid lover's fish room.

"Pelmatochromis" thomasi above (Photo by Ruda Zukal) and *"Hemichromis" bimaculatus* below (Photo by G. Marcuse) will shortly be united into a new genus.

Spawning of a recently imported forest form of *"Hemichromis" bimaculatus*. The common name, jewelfish, is an understatement. Photos by Hans J. Richter.

The *thomasi* species has recently been described as bred among European aquarists, but American reports of this species have so far all seemed to be erroneous. A relatively peaceful species, but not nearly as attractive as the related jewel fish. It does not have the hanging pad in the pharynx, is sexually dull (breeding without going to the trouble to make a formal nest, and being a poor parent), lacks microgillrakers, and has a few other characters which will probably also go into the generic definition when it appears.

THE GENUS *HEMICHROMIS*

As pointed out previously, *H. bimaculatus* will be removed from this genus, leaving only *H. fasciatus* (Peters, 1857) the type of the genus. Thus, the discussion will be restricted to this fish only.

First, it appears that *H. fasciatus* is actually comprised of two species in nature. These fishes are virtually identical when preserved but, according to Paul Loiselle, are found in different habitats in nature and apparently do not interbreed. Which one is the fish originally considered by Peters to be the type of his genus is not known at the present time. The far less common and larger type is referred to as *H. fasciatus* Type A, while the smaller, more common, and prettier type is called *H. fasciatus* Type B. *H. fasciatus* Type A has sometimes been confused with other fishes, and I have seen an adult pair with the label

Hemichromis fasciatus type "B." Photo by Chvojka Milan.

"Pelmatochromis arnoldi," a name which is a synonym for *Thysia ansorgii.* The Type B form adult has much more red in its sides, usually arranged in horizontal rows of dots, and is the form likely to be seen by aquarists. *Hemichromis* can be recognized by the enlarged teeth at the midline of the jaws. The A form has a bright red throat and breast, but no red dots on its sides. It breeds like the B form.

H. fasciatus Type B is an excellent parent, a typical substratum brooder, hard surface spawner, and territorial fish. Young specimens frequently appear in shops as "Lake Tanganyika cichlids" or "Tanga Cichlids." Such names are misleading. The fish is West-Central African in distribution, ranging somewhat northward and southward, but it never occurs in the Great Rift Valley Lakes. Any fish which costs less than a dollar (or less than five!) cannot really be a Lake Tanganyika cichlid, and the aquarist should use some sense before leaping to a bargain! The B form extends eastward into the Zambezi basin.

The juveniles are usually ragged (they fight among themselves continually), and have a series of about five spots or bands on each side. The tail fin (what's left of it) is symmetrical, the mouth is large, and the fish are active and aggressive. Growth is rapid and large size is attained. They should have a meaty diet, lots of room, and frequent massive water changes. Many will be killed by their brothers and sisters, but eventually the aquarist will be left with at least a pair provided he starts with about half a dozen to a dozen juveniles. Each pair should have its own tank of not less than twenty or thirty gallons and the eggs and fry may remain with the parents.

Breeding is not remarkable. A hard substratum, such as the bottom of the tank or a flat plate, is scrubbed for several days. The female lays several hundred to more than a thousand eggs, tending in concentric circles. The pair guards the eggs and young viciously, and will kill or severely damage anything else in the tank at this time. Moving the parents with the fry to another tank will not frighten the fish into eating their fry (probably nothing will). Just as you think you are about to raise a thousand fish, the fry begin fighting among one another, reducing their numbers significantly.

A lovely but rough fish, recommended for the devoted cichlido-

Hemichromis fasciatus type "A." Upper photo by Dr. Herbert R. Axelrod; lower photo by Wolfgang Bechtle.

Hemichromis fasciatus, type "A," young form. Photo by Dr. Herbert R. Axelrod.

Pelvicachromis sp.

phile. The fry can be used as food for other fishes, as they are more numerous than anyone would wish. Four to five inches maximal size in aquaria and perhaps somewhat larger in nature for the B form. The A form may attain fifteen inches in nature.

THE GENUS *NANOCHROMIS*

The genus *Nanochromis* (Pellegrin, 1904) is entirely West African in distribution, and makes up a moderately sized natural assemblage of species. See Loiselle (1970) and Thys (1968) for details. These are generally small, elongate cichlids lacking the fleshy pad previously used to define the old genus *Pelmatochromis*, in which a number of these forms had been placed because of less than careful study. The gillrakers are broadly tuberculate on the first gill arch; microgillrakers are absent. Sexually dimorphic and dichromatic substratum spawners; no mouthbrooders known; spawning typically occurs in a cave, and the eggs are oblong and white or tan, attached to the hard substratum by a strong thread. Females tend to court more than males, and to be more colorful. According to Loiselle (1970) and Thys (pers. communication) the following species are included in the genus:

nudiceps Pellegrin, 1904 (the type species of the genus)
longirostris (Boulenger, 1903)
caudifasciatus (Boulenger, 1913)
dimidiatus (Pellegrin, 1900)
robertsi (Thys and Loiselle, 1970)
cavalliensis (Thys and Loiselle, 1970)

The fish called *N. squamiceps* Boulenger, 1902 is probably the same as *N. dimidiatus*, and should be considered a junior synonym of the latter. *N. dimidiatus* is relatively new to the hobby, the first major imports occurring in 1969–1970. Aquarists had a good deal of trouble breeding this fish at first, for a very good reason. The first imports appeared to consist of all males. As these fish did vary somewhat, aquarists were eyeballing "pairs" based on differences that had nothing to do with sex. Shortly thereafter females began coming in with the males, and a number of people succeeded in spawning the fish. Males tend to an overall orange coloration, most richly developed on the belly and forward region. Unpaired fins are heavily banded. The lips are blood-red. Females

Nanochromis nudiceps, male. Photo by Hilmar Hansen.

Nanochromis dimidiatus, female, not in nuptial coloration. Photo by Gunter Senfft.

Nanochromis dimidiatus. Single specimen. Photo by Dr. Herbert R. Axelrod.

Nanochromis dimidiatus, pair. Male above. Photo by Dr. Herbert R. Axelrod.

Nanochromis nudiceps pair with fry. Photo by Hans Joachim Richter. The ovipositor is still visible in this female *Nanochromis nudiceps* as she cares for her young. Photo by Hans Joachim Richter.

tend to a purplish color, with a silvery spot on the dorsal fin. Males are aggressive toward one another when attempting to establish or defend territories. The tank should be richly filled with rockwork and caves, and cleanliness is quite important.

These fish are picky eaters and seem to relish the fry of other fishes. Live foods highly recommended. *N. dimidiatus* originally came in under all kinds of strange names, including *Polychrominus dimitri*. Such names have no standing and should be ignored. They indicate that the original identification was correct, but the exporter had a rather confusing penmanship. In my opinion, this is the most beautiful West African cichlid to appear in the hobby in years, and it is hoped that it becomes as thoroughly established as *N. nudiceps*.

Nanochromis nudiceps may seem like an oldtimer to relatively new aquarists, but in fact it has not been known in the hobby that long. Many people still recall the first importations. This striking beauty is generally blue-green and white below, with rich iridescence on the flanks. Females are much more colorful than males. In this species (but not in *N. dimidiatus*), females always look rather heavy with spawn and always (in good health) have the ovipositor protruding. Before an actual spawning the tube will descend much further and the female will become enormously distended rather than just fat.

Subuni Junction on Lake Volta. Photo by Paul V. Loiselle.

Neither species is especially easy to induce to breed, but *N. nudiceps* appears considerably more difficult than *N. dimidiatus*. Both species are cave spawners and should have a large tank if the parents are to be allowed to raise the young. I recommend artificial hatching, however, and raising away from the parents if you wish to be sure of raising a good number. If the other species of *Nanochromis* are as striking as the two aquarium species described above, the genus will get the prize for the most beautiful cichlids of West Africa. Watch for new imports at your shop.

THE GENUS *PELVICACHROMIS*

Pelvicachromis Thys, 1968 contains the fishes previously known to aquarists as the dwarf *Pelmatochromis* forms, typified by the well-known fish called *kribensis*. In part, the genus is defined as possessing a fleshy pad hanging from the roof of the mouth, gillrakers on first gill arch lanceolate, microgillrakers absent, sexually dichromatic and dimorphic. The species in this new genus include:

humilis (Boulenger, 1916)
pulcher (Boulenger, 1901)
roloffi (Thys, 1968)
taeniatus (Boulenger, 1901)
subocellatus (Günther, 1871)
Several unnamed species, to be named in the future.

Pelvicachromis humilis occurs in Sierra Leone and Guinea, but only in the southeastern part of the latter country. This fish has a very restricted range. Mr. E. Roloff of Germany has this fish in aquaria and perhaps breeding stock will eventually circulate in this country, if he successfully spawns them.

Pelvicachromis roloffi occurs in Sierra Leone and East Guinea, but has not yet gotten into the hobby. Very similar to *P. pulcher*.

Pelvicachromis subocellatus occurs from lower Gabon to the lower part of The Congo. The tail fin resembles that of *P. taeniatus*, but there the similarity ends. The female becomes almost black in the front and rear during nuptial displays, and her belly region becomes a rich lavender. Occasionally imported, but apparently not established in the tanks of American aquarists.

Pelvicachromis taeniatus is not as common in the hobby as some others of its genus, but it is not rare either. Unfortunately, almost

Pelvicachromis pulcher, female. Photo by Stanislav Frank.

Pelvicachromis pulcher, male. Photo by Dr. Herbert R. Axelrod.

A pink variety of *Pelvicachromis pulcher*. This is a male specimen. Photo by Dr. Herbert R. Axelrod.

Pelvicachromis cf. *humilis*, resembling the form found in the Kasewe forest of West Africa. Photo by Dr. Herbert R. Axelrod.

any richly marked strain of *P. pulcher* is often called *taeniatus* by aquarists engaged in wishful thinking. This is probably also the source of the frequent rumors of hybridizations between *taeniatus* and "*kribensis*," probably all of which can be considered matings between different forms of *P. pulcher*. Of considerable interest was Thys's (1968) finding that the name *Pelmatochromis kribensis* was in fact a junior synonym for *Pelvicachromis taeniatus*. Thus, the specific epithet *kribensis* should not be used.

Pelvicachromis pulcher is the correct name for the fish long called *kribensis* in the aquarium hobby, and every cichlidophile is familiar with the species. It is about time the name *pulcher* caught on and *kribensis* was forgotten.

The giant krib is the colloquial name assigned to a fish presently without a scientific name, but well-known in the hobby. This fish may also be referred to as *P.* sp. aff. *pulcher*, or *P. cf. pulcher*. The use of *cf.* or of *sp. aff.* simply means that the fish is closely related to, but not identical with, the species indicated by the final epithet. In the present case it indicates that the giant krib is without a scientific name, but it bears a close relationship to the

Pelvicachromis taeniatus. Photo by Gunter Senfft.

A female *Lamprologus mocquardi*. Photo by Curt Dunbar.

regular *pulcher*. This fish is larger, hardier, and much more intensively pigmented than *P. pulcher*. The reds are much deeper and the blacks more intense. There is an overall bronze cast to the body.

Two forms of males are known, as first pointed out by Heiligenberg (1965) and subsequently by Thys (1968). In the first form the red coloration of the belly extends all the way to the tip of the nose, making the entire ventrum blood red. In the second type, the ventral red area is much more limited, not getting beyond the insertion of the pectorals and often not even coming close. Both types are found in the same waters, and this is not a subspecific difference. Aquarists continue to confuse the second type with the true *pulcher* (an understandable error), but the first type cannot be confused with anything else.

There are a number of additional species known,but not named, in this genus, and they are often referred to by *cf., sp. aff.,* or geographic designations. One of these is *P.* cf. *subocellatus* from southern Nigeria. A number of these fishes will be given legal names in the near future, and this will simplify the nomenclature. The names *aureocephalus, camerunensis,* and *klugei* should be discarded, as they are today without any merit.

Pelvicachromis taeniatus.

Pelvicachromis taeniatus, formerly known under the name *Pelmato-chromis klugei*. Upper photo by Hilmar Hansen of the Aquarium Berlin. Lower photo by Dr. Herbert R. Axelrod.

As far as is known, all species of *Pelvicachromis* are cave spawners on hard substrata, usually the walls or ceiling of a cave. The cave should be deep and the aquarium filled with much rockwork. Some pairs (irrespective of the species) are good parents, while most are not. Thus, artificial handling of the eggs and fry is recommended for the first or second spawnings. The eggs are tan, with a light spot distal and a dark thread proximal to the substratum, by which they are attached to the rock. The pre-nuptial behavior is very long and drawn out, but the aquarist can sometimes speed things up with mild heat and abundant living foods. Above all, the cave provided ought to be as deep as possible, as these fishes are generally shy and secretive when spawning. As in *Nanochromis,* it is the female that generally does most of the courting, and is the more colorful.

Hatching generally occurs in about three days. In about a week the fry begin scooting about on the bottom, and in another day or so they become free-swimming, and behave as a shoal. Aquarists often observe that a spawn is practically all males or all females. Heiligenberg (1965) pointed this out also, and noted that breeding at pH 4 to 5 (acid water) seemed to produce 90% males, while breeding in neutral water produced 90% females. The water should thus be varied or maintained slightly acidic. Probably sperm cells have differing viability at different pH values according to whether they carry an X or a Y chromosome, so that very acid water tends to inactivate sperm cells carrying the X chromosome; this is only conjecture.

THE GENUS *LAMPROLOGUS*

Lamprologus Schilthuis, 1891 is a large and diversified genus occurring in both the Congo River drainage system and Lake Tanganyika. The Lake Tanganyika species will be covered under the discussion of that lake, and the others will be covered in this section. An early but comprehensive review of the genus, as known in 1915, was presented by G. A. Boulenger in his famous *Catalogue of the Fresh-Water Fishes of Africa (Volume III)*. Boulenger defined the genus, generally, as of various shapes; with strongly denticulate scales and the scales of the nape and adjacent area of the back being quite small; teeth conical and forming a villiform band, with canines in the front of each jaw. He presented other characters as well. Of interest are the small scales behind the head, which are very apparent in all the drawings in the literature. A partial listing of the Congo drainage species would include the following:

	Dorsal	Anal	Range
congolensis	XVIII–XIX/8–10	VI–VII/5–6	Entire Congo
tumbanus	XVII–XVIII/8–9	V–VI/5–6	Upper Congo
mocquardii	XIX/8	V–VI/6–7	Upper Ubangi
werneri	XIX/9	VI/6	Lower Congo

All the species have five or six dark cross bars, and the coloration varies from yellowish gray to purplish brown. I know of no reliable characters to separate the species from the Congo. They all overlap in meristics and morphometrics.

L. congolensis Schilthuis, 1891 was the first species to be described in this genus. It is the fish previously known in the hobby as *mocquardi,* and is a rough customer. Occasionally bred. *L. tumbanus* Mathes, 1964 is found in Lake Tumba and is uncommon in the hobby. *L. mocquardi* Pellegrin, 1903 is little known, but

Lamprologus werneri. Photo by Hilmar Hansen, Aquarium Berlin.

Lamprologus elongatus of Lake Tanganyika. Photo by Hilmar Hansen, Aquarium Berlin.

Lamprologus attenuatus is a common bottom nester from Lake Tanganyika. Photo by R. J. Goldstein.

Lamprologus mocquardi, from the upper Ubangi branch of the Congo River. Photo by Klaus Paysan.

Lamprologus sp. Photo by Dr. Herbert R. Axelrod.

Leptotilapia irvinei, male, from the Volta River in West Africa. Photo by Paul V. Loiselle.

apparently is in the hobby. *L. werneri* Poll, 1959 is imported occasionally as a *Teleogramma* species. See Lindquist (1971) for a comprehensive review.

THE GENUS *LEPTOTILAPIA*

Leptotilapia Pellegrin, 1928 is a genus of shovel-mouthed bottom-hopping cichlids, from West Africa. It contains at least the two species *L. tinanti* Pellegrin, 1928 and *L. irvinei* (Trewavas, 1943). The former is well-known in the hobby, having appeared some fifteen years ago under its old and no-longer-used generic name *Gobiochromis*. I know of no breeding reports, but the fish is commonly imported from Africa. *L. irvinei* occurs in the Volta Basin and I suspect *L. tinanti* is Congolese. *L. tinanti* is light gray with a tendency for its five or so dusky bands to be interrupted by a horizontal streak of lighter coloration along the flank. *L. irvinei* is greenish gray with about seven of these indistinct bands (Roman, 1965) and has apparently not yet been imported.

THE GENUS *TELEOGRAMMA*

Teleogramma Boulenger contains three species of Congo River cichlids characterized by a bottom dwelling habit. They generally live under rocks, etc., in swift streams, much as do many of our native freshwater sculpins. These are large-mouthed, elongate fishes and one of them *T. brichardi,* has been bred in aquaria. See Wickler (1959). The species are distinguished by a few characters.

	Dorsal	Anal	Scales in Ll.
brichardi Poll	XXIV/7	V/10	60
gracile Boulenger	XXIII/8	VI/7	35
monogramma (Pellegrin)	XX/10	IV/10	34–35

These species also differ in the dimensions of the caudal peduncle. Recall from the early part of this book that the caudal peduncle length is measured from the base of the anal fin to the base of the caudal fin. The depth of the caudal peduncle is the least depth. In *T. monogramma* the caudal peduncle is longer than deep; in *T. gracile* as long as deep; and in *T. brichardi* deeper than long. The only breeding and color information available is that of Wickler.

Teleogramma brichardi, named in honor of Pierre Brichard, the famous African collector.

Lamprologus compressiceps of Lake Tanganyika. Photo by W. Hoppe.

Lamprologus savoryi of Lake Tanganyika. Photo by Dr. Herbert R. Axelrod.

Teleogramma brichardi of the Congo River. Photo by P. Brichard.

Leptotilapia tinanti of the Congo River. Photo by Dr. Herbert R. Axelrod.

Males have a thin white border to the upper part of the caudal and dorsal fins. In females the white is far better developed, and the area on the caudal fin expands into a white patch with some red. Both sexes are very dark overall. At spawning time the female develops a red girdle, much like the coloration in females of *Pelvicachromis subocellatus*. The female, the more colorful of the two, sets up the territory (a cave) and the male enters for brief periods. At these times she courts him (instead of the other way around) and a pair bond finally forms. Eventually spawning occurs to yield a small number of large, adhesive eggs stuck to the roof or walls of the cave. Hatching occurs in three days, but before this time the male is driven off, and the female has all but sealed up her cave with gravel.

Recall that in the substratum nesters the male and female are often marked similarly, whereas in mouthbrooders of the maternal type it is the male who sets up the territory and courts, and is the more colorful of the two. In the case of *T. brichardi* we have a different situation. As the territory defender the female becomes more colorful and the male is driven off. But she does not mouthbrood, although her protection of the eggs and young is probably equally as efficient. As she is doing the courting, a male may mate many times in a season in nature, but the system does not lend itself to rapid speciation.

THE GENUS *STEATOCRANUS*

Steatocranus Boulenger, 1899 is a Congo River genus characterized by the following: moderately elongate body; two widely separated series of notched teeth in both jaws; the outer series of teeth larger and with one or two pairs of larger, truncate, incisor-like teeth at the symphysis (middle of the jaw); a fatty gibbosity may occur on the head.

The original species in this genus was named *S. gibbiceps*. It is just a brownish fish. Counts: D XIX-XX/8, A III/6. Upper lateral line scales, 21; lower lateral line scales, 10-11.

S. casuarius Poll, 1939 has the same D and A counts and coloration, and is known in the hobby as the blockhead, lumphead or lionhead cichlid. This is a gentle fish, not difficult to breed, but it ought to be set up in a tank with much rockwork and gravel

Steatocranus casuarius is a shy bottom-dwelling species of the Congo River that is easily bred in aquaria. Photo of male (above) by Ruda Zukal. Photo of female (below) by G. Marcuse.

The most recent opinion (of many!) identifies the Congo River cichlid shown here as *Steatocranus elongatus*. Photo by Dr. R. J. Goldstein.

Steatocranus casuarius, male above with the beginning of a frontal gibbosity. At this point he is mature enough to spawn. Photo by Stanislav Frank.

This flowerpot provides an ideal spawning site for this pair of *Steatocranus casuarius*. Photo by Stanislav Frank.

A male *Steatocranus casuarius* with a well developed frontal gibbosity. Photo by Dr. Herbert R. Axelrod.

so that it can construct a cave. Typical substratum breeders. It can also be bred in a bare tank with a flower pot cave.

S. elongatus may be the correct name of the fish circulating as *Leptotilapia* sp., according to Paul Loiselle, but I have not seen any literature on this nominal species.

THE GENUS *SARGOCHROMIS*

Sargochromis Regan, 1920 is a *Tilapia*-like genus, but can be distinguished by its massive pharyngeal teeth (which look like almost confluent boils) and short, stout gill rakers. *S. codringtoni* (Boulenger, 1908) is from the Zambezi and Kafue Rivers, and attains six pounds in weight. *S. angolensis* (Steindachner, 1865) is similar, and found in the Cunene River. *S. giardi* (Pellegrin, 1904) occurs in the Upper Zambezi, Mashi, Okavango and Kafue Rivers. It attains a weight of six pounds and probably feeds on mussels and snails. All information on this genus is from Jubb (1967). *S. giardi* has also been known as *Pelmatochromis robustus*. *S. codringtoni* has been known incorrectly as *Paratilapia marginata*.

THE GENUS *SERRANOCHROMIS*

Serranochromis Regan, 1920 contains a number of species previously placed in the old genus *Paratilapia*. The genus has about the same distribution as *Sargochromis*. All of them are large predators from the lakes and rivers of central and southern Africa, where they are highly regarded as game fishes. See Jubb (1967) for details. Probably all mouthbrooders. The species include: *S. robustus* (syns: *Pelmatochromis ngamensis, Paratilapia zambeziensis*); *S. macrocephalus* (syns: *Pelmatochromis genisquamulatus, Paratilapia ellenbergi*); *S. longimanus; S. angusticeps* (syn: *Paratilapia kafuensis*); *S. thumbergi*.

Serranochromis robustus also occurs in Lake Malawi. A subspecies is widely distributed through the upper and middle Zambezi system, where it attains thirteen pounds in weight, and bears a remarkable resemblance to American black basses. Known to be a mouthbrooder. All other species of the genus are smaller, ranging from three to five pounds as their upper weight limits. See also the discussion of the Cunene River. The genus is characterized by short, sometimes T-shaped, and heavy gillrakers on the first gill arch; two rows of widely spaced heavy, conical teeth; and a very high scale count.

The most important work on this genus is that of Trewavas (1964), in which she reviewed the entire genus, provided updated descriptions of the species, described *S. stappersi, S. spei* and *S. janus*, and discussed the habitats and distribution of the species of the genus. A number of zoo-geographical generalizations became evident, which were as follows. First, there is an apparent unity of the fish fauna of the Cunene, Kafue and Upper Zambezi Rivers. Further, there is a partial interchange of species at the origins of the Upper Zambezi and Kafue on the one hand and the Congo River system on the other hand. This is because the origins of these independent systems are in a swampy plateau rather than mountains. There was also some similarity noted of the fishes of the Upper Zambezi and Kafue with fishes of the Lake Bangweulu region (see *Cichlids of Smaller African Làkes*, p. 306).

Serranochromis contains species found in shallow, reedy lakes and swamps; they occur in some large African lakes, but probably only in reedy shoreline areas. See Trewavas (1964) for a key to the species, and further details of anatomy and distribution.

Lamprologus sp. All the species in this genus are bottom nesters. Photo by Gerhard Marcuse.

Hemihaplochromis philander is behaviorally quite different from *H. multicolor*, and according to Dr. R. A. Jubb might even have to be transferred to *Pseudocrenilabrus*, as defined by Fowler in 1934. Photo above by H. Hansen.

Hemihaplochromis multicolor. Upper photo by Hilmar Hansen, Aquarium Berlin. Lower photo by Wolfgang Bechtle.

THE GENUS *CHETIA*

Chetia Trewavas, 1961 is very similar to *Serranochromis*. It differs from *Serranochromis* in having only a single row of conical, widely-spaced teeth. *C. flaviventris* is restricted to the Limpopo and Incomati Rivers, and attains a foot in length. *C. brevis* occurs in the Komati and Lomati Rivers. These rivers generally have southeast African drainages into the Indian Ocean in the region of Mozambique. The largest basin of all is the Limpopo River system, emptying somewhat to the south of the great Zambezi River, itself of considerably greater importance.

THE GENUS *HEMIHAPLOCHROMIS*

The genus *Hemihaplochromis* Wickler, 1963 was defined to contain those species, previously included in *Haplochromis*, that had a couple of characters considered to be of generic importance. First, some scales in the lateral line lack pores. But more important, behaviorally, is the absence in *Hemihaplochromis* of ocelli on the anal fin of the adult male. The posterior tip of the fin is the same color as the spots near its base. All female mouthbrooders.

Hemihaplochromis contains very few species, including:

multicolor (Hilgendorf, 1903): Egyptian mouthbrooder.
strigigena (Pfeffer, 1893): Egyptian mouthbrooder.
philander (Weber, 1897): Dwarf bream.

According to Sterba (1963), *H. strigigena* is a synonym of *H. multicolor*, but Sterba used *multicolor* as the valid name; this is incorrect, for if the two are indeed the same species then *strigigena* would take priority as the older of the two names. *H. strigigena* and/or *H. multicolor* occur in the Nile drainage throughout north Africa, whereas *H. philander* occurs from deep southern Africa northward, even into the Congo drainage.

In Wickler's view (1966, and earlier), this genus lacks true egg dummies, which were defined as spots surrounded by a border of contrasting color. Aquarists know such spots as ocelli. In the presence of ocelli (apparently occurring in *Haplochromis* and some of its derivatives) the female snaps at these marks (which are supposed to resemble either eggs or "super-eggs") during spawning, thereby inhaling sperm and assuring fertilization of the eggs after they get into her mouth; further, the eggs are most likely not fertilized during spawning except in this way. *I do not accept this thesis.*

THE GENUS *HAPLOCHROMIS*

The genus *Haplochromis* Hilgendorf, 1888 is the largest genus of the family Cichlidae, with an enormous number of species distributed throughout Africa, although most heavily concentrated toward the east. The group is so large that it is difficult to present a set of defining characteristics without including, time and again, the modifier, *usually*. The major character setting off *Haplochromis* and its derivatives is the formation of the apophysis, a bony fusion between the skull and palate. In this fish group, the fusion of bones consists of the basioccipital and the paraspenoids, whereas in the *Tilapia* line of evolution, the basioccipital is not involved. Other than that, the scales are usually ctenoid (in *Tilapia* they may be ctenoid or cycloid); teeth in two or more series, the outer bicuspid or conical (in *Tilapia* one does not usually encounter conical teeth in the outer series); inner teeth usually tricuspid (same as *Tilapia*); maxillary bone exposed at the end when the mouth is closed (usually hidden under similar circumstances in *Tilapia*, with some exceptions). The various and numerous related genera are obviously derived from a *Haplochromis*-like ancestor, and are distinguished primarily by their dentition. These various kinds of dentition are apparently trophic (feeding) modifications of every conceivable kind.

We usually think of explosive speciation as having occurred in the Great Lakes of Africa, but it has apparently occurred in smaller lakes associated with the western river systems. For example, in Lake Fwa and the River Fwa (near a southern branch of the Congo River), may be found *Haplochromis brauschi*, *H. callichromis*, and *H. rheophilus*, in addition to smaller, derived genera and species, viz., *Cyclopharynx fwae* (=*Callopharynx microdon*), *Neopharynx schwetzi*, and *Schwetzochromis neodon*. These fishes bear startling resemblance to some of the *Haplochromis* derivatives of Lake Tanganyika. Also in the region of the lower Congo are *Haplochromis polli* and some others. For details see Poll (1948) and Poll and Thys (1965). Other species of *Haplochromis* are

Haplochromis cf. *heterotaenia* (above), and *Haplochromis ericotaenia* (below). Photos by Michael K. Oliver.

Haplochromis epichorialis (above), and *Haplochromis callipterus* (below). Photos by Michael K. Oliver.

found in some (but not all) of the African lakes. An enormous number of species of this and associated genera have given rise to the great species flock of Lake Malawi, whereas in Lake Tanganyika both *Haplochromis* and *Tilapia* kinds of ancestors gave rise to at least a dual species flock.

Wickler (1966) points out that, in this genus (*Haplochromis*), egg dummies occur on the anal fin of the male, and this is required for oral fertilization of the eggs in the female. In my view the genus is too large for any such sweeping statement. Further, whereas anal fin ocelli may often function as egg dummies, it is inconceivable to me that they should be necessary for fertilization. Wickler (1966) has stated:

> "The males of *Haplochromis* and related mouthbrooding species bear very conspicuous yellow or orange spots near the base of the anal fin. . . . These spots resemble the eggs of the particular species in colour, size and form. They are displayed to the female during courtship and during fertilization and elicit her reaction of snapping up eggs. During courtship they make the male more attractive to the female. In spawning they assure fertilization of the eggs, which are taken into the female's mouth immediately after they have been laid *and before the male is able to fertilize them.* In snapping at the 'egg spots' with her lips, the female inhales the sperm, thus fertilizing the eggs within her mouth." [Italics mine.]

Aside from all the obvious "egg dummies" in other mouthbrooding species, their presence in females as well as males, their variation from spots to blotches with or without ocelli, and the other nuptial colors of males in addition to those of the anal fin, I should also like to point out that I have observed a hybridization between *Pseudotropheus auratus* (male) and *P. tropheops* (female) in which both fishes spawned in a fifty-gallon aquarium *by themselves* at the same approximate time, and came nowhere near each other. Yet, there was sufficient sperm in the water to effect fertilization of the eggs. The hybrids proved to be fertile.

Wickler's hypothesis could use some additional help! For example, oral fertilization would be more tenable if it could be shown that these mouthbrooders released sperm in the form of packets, rather than as free cells. But such data are not available. I am prepared to accept that anal spots may enhance the reproductive act, but not that they are necessary nor that the female snaps up eggs before they can be fertilized. Sperm penetration precedes egg activation, and if Wickler means to define fertilization

Haplochromis nigricans, male, from Lake Victoria. The entire caudal fin and the light spots on the edge of the dorsal fin are actually brilliant red, while the body is deep blue with lighter blue bands. Photo by Paul V. Loiselle.

Haplochromis sp. Photo by G. Marcuse.

Haplochromis cf. *macrostoma*, from Lake Malawi. Photo by Michael K. Oliver.

Haplochromis modestus (Günther). Lake Malawi. Photo bv Michael K. Oliver.

Haplochromis livingstonii (Günther). Monkey Bay, Malawi. Photo by Michael K. Oliver.

Callochromis sp. Photo by Dr. Herbert R. Axelrod.

as *both* phenomena, rather than simply attachment leading to penetration, then his conclusion becomes correct, but misleading in its context.

A rather new and popular species to the hobby is *Haplochromis burtoni*. For information on this species see Leong (1969) and Zukal (1971).

Before looking at the species flocks of the Great Lakes, let us look at the cichlids known from other smaller lakes throughout Africa.

CICHLIDS OF SMALLER AFRICAN LAKES

LAKE	CICHLID FAUNA
NAIVASHA: immediately below the equator and due east from L. Victoria. Area, 80 square miles. Depth, 20–25 meters. Altitude, 6,230 feet.	*Tilapia leucosticta* and two other species of *Tilapia*, all introduced. Breeding is seasonal and correlated with maximal sunshine and heat. (Hyder, 1969.)
KYOGA: directly north of Lake Victoria. Large, and lying in a swamplike region. Connected to Lake Albert by a river that is interrupted by Murcheson Falls.	*Haplochromis worthingtoni*. (For the distribution of the many species of *Tilapia* in Africa, see Thys, 1968.)
LAKE GANGU: probably due south of Lake Edward.	*Tilapia eduardiana* and perhaps other Lake Edward fishes.
LAKE NABUGABO: two miles west of Lake Victoria, cut off from Victoria 4,000 years ago. Endemic species marked with an asterisk. (Greenwood, 1964.)	*Hemihaplochromis multicolor* *Astatoreochromis alluadi* *Tilapia esculenta* *T. variabilis* *Haplochromis nubilus* *H. venator** *H. velifer** *H. simpsoni** *H. beadlei** *H. annectidens**
LAKE MWERU: due west of the southern part of L. Tanganyika.	*Tylochromis mylodon* *Haplochromis moeruensis* *Serranochromis macrocephala*

The Rift Valley System of Africa

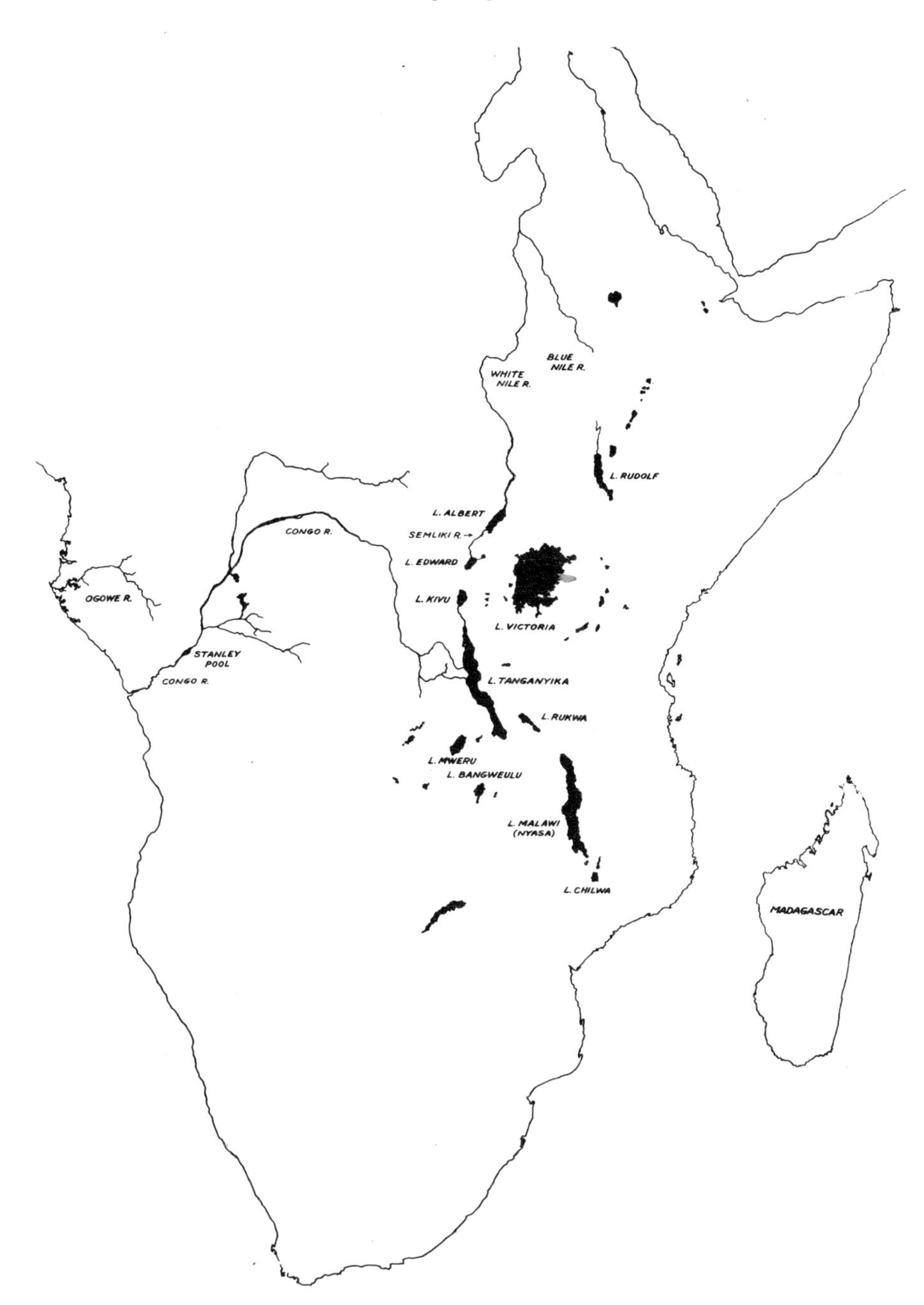

Haplochromis spilostichus Trewavas 1935. 12·2 cm standard length. Trawled August 5, 1971 off Chembe village, Malawi, in 10–16 fathoms. Photo by Michael K. Oliver.

Member of the "Utaka", a group of zooplankton-feeding species of *Haplochromis* in Lake Malawi.

Haplochromis polystigma. Lake Malawi. Leopard cichlid (adult). Photo by Michael K. Oliver.

Haplochromis woodi. Lake Malawi. Photo by Michael K. Oliver.

LAKE NGAMI: below the 20th parallel, in Bechuanaland. Quite southerly compared with other lakes.	*Serranochromis longimanus* *S. thumbergii* *Haplochromis gibbiceps* *H. frederici* *H. smithii*
LAKE BANGWEULU: SSE of Lake Tanganyika, and west of Lake Malawi. No endemic species except perhaps the single *Tylochromis* species.	*Tylochromis bangwelensis* *Haplochromis mellandi* *Serranochromis angusticeps* *S. thumbergi*
LAKE BAROMBI-MA-MBU: (Cameroon).[1] Probably all endemic.	*Barombia maclareni* *Stomatepia mariae* *Stomatepia* sp. *Tilapia linnellii* *T. steinbachi* *T. eisentrauti* *T. lohnbergeri (=T. caroli)*
LAKE BAROMBI-BA-KOTTO: (Cameroon).[1] *Tilapia kottae* and *Chromidotilapia loennbergi* are endemic.	*Tilapia kottae* *T. mariae* *T. galilaea multifasciata* *Chromidotilapia loennbergi*
LAKE EJAGHAM: (Cameroon).[1]	*Tilapia deckerti* (endemic)
LAKE BASUMTWI: (Ghana).[1] Probably only *T. discolor* is endemic.	*Tilapia discolor* *T. busumana* *T. multifasciata* *Hemichromis fasciatus* *Chromidotilapia guentheri*
LAKE FWA: (Congo).[1] See Poll (1948). All endemic except *Hemichromis*.	*Neopharynx schwetzi* *Schwetzochromis neodon* (this genus may be a synonym for *Neopharynx)* *Cyclopharynx fwae (=Callopharynx microdon)* *Haplochromis brauschi* *H. rheophilus* *H. callichromis* *Hemichromis fasciatus*

[1] Data from Dr. Dirk Thys v.d. Audenaerde (pers. comm.).

THE GREAT LAKES OF EAST AFRICA

The eastern portion of the great African continent is one of the most fascinating and geologically diverse regions of the world. Its fish fauna is no less interesting, and the majority of the cichlids of the world occur here. The oldest rocks lie exposed in this region, and it is here that biological history reads clearest. Olduvai Gorge, where Dr. Leakey found the oldest of humans, lies in this region. And off the coast in the Indian Ocean is found that Devonian relict, the coelacanth. The swamps contain species of *Nothobranchius*, bizarrely colored killifishes (family Cyprinodontidae) and lungfishes, both surviving desiccation by hibernating in the mud (lungfishes) or producing drought-resistant eggs (killifishes). To the north is the ancient kingdom of Ethiopia, and human history is, in this part of the world, old and based on a much higher civilization than anywhere else on the continent with the possible exception of the Nile Delta.

The nations of the region broke the bonds of colonialism through, in several cases, notorious violence. The many peoples of these several nations are fiercely independent and tribal differences blend only with difficulty. Much of the romance of Africa, to Americans, is based on an east African background, including Mount Kilimanjaro, Mount Kenya, and the vast veldts with their rich game of elephant, lion, wildebeest, zebra, giraffe, hippo, rhino, and the horror of sleeping sickness carried by tsetse flies. What would America be without Edgar Rice Burroughs' *Tarzan*, and what would Tarzan be without East Africa?

The eastern section of the continent is geologically taken up by the Great Rift Valley, which is actually a group of valleys and mountain chains extending from the tip of the Arabian Peninsula, down the continent, and well into the Indian Ocean. In the north, where the Red Sea meets the Gulf of Aden, a great valley between a paired mountain chain rises high into the sky and swings southwestward. Another mountain-valley combination begins far to the east and south, and extends in a clockwise arc down the continent. Much of the land between these two Great Rift Valleys is taken up by the enormous but shallow Lake Victoria. It is located between, but not within, the rifts. There are many other

Haplochromis moorii. Adult. The black fin stripes are not natural. Captured along the sandy shores of Lake Malawi on hook and line. Photo by Michael K. Oliver.

Haplochromis sp. (probably *H. kirkii*). Photo by Hilmar Hansen, Aquarium Berlin.

Haplochromis strigatus. Sandy shores of Lake Malawi. Photo by Michael K. Oliver.

Haplochromis euchilus from Lake Malawi. Photo by Hilmar Hansen, Aquarium Berlin.

lakes in this region, but the most exciting ones are the big ones, including Victoria and the true Rift Lakes, Albert, Edward, Kivu, Malawi and Tanganyika. We will discuss the lakes individually, for each is a biological, as well as geological, marvel. For general information on the lakes of this region, see Beauchamp (1964), Greenwood (1964) and Fryer and Iles (1969). For detailed geological data, see Girdler et al (1969).

The western rift contains Lakes Rukwa, Tanganyika, Kivu, Edward, Albert and Malawi. The eastern or Gregory rift contains the smaller Lakes Balangida, Manyara, Natron, Magadi, Naivasha, Nakuru, Hannington, and Baringo. Except for some introduced species of *Tilapia* in L. Naivasha, little is known of the fishes of the Gregory rift, and our discussion will be limited to the larger lakes of the western rift.

LAKE ALBERT

Lake Albert is connected to the Upper Nile, a great river that also has influenced the fish fauna of Lake Victoria. One of the shallow rift lakes, Lake Albert has a maximal depth of only 144 feet. It is 1,640 square miles in area, and this massive size lends it to one of the rift lake phenomena regarding winds and rainfall. In

Haplochromis lividus, male, from Lake Victoria. Similar markings occur on several other species from this lake, and from the Nile River. Photo by Paul V. Loiselle.

the morning warm air rises from the lake, and the winds from the shore heading out lakeward carry with them swarms of lake flies of the families Chironomidae and Chaoboridae. Many other insects are swept out over the water with these offshore winds. The African name for Lake Albert translates to "destroyer of locusts." Ascending air currents far out on the lake carry the insects rather high up, and ultimately these fall into the lake to drown or be devoured by the fishes.

The same phenomenon is observed in Lakes Victoria and Malawi (but not L. Tanganyika), and the clouds of ascending insects look like bush fires several miles out on the lakes (Beauchamp, 1964).

A lake of this size would be expected to have a rich fish fauna, and it does. There are 37 non-cichlid species, and ten cichlid species, of which five are endemic to this lake (occurring here and nowhere else). These are *Tilapia galilaea, T. zillii, T. nilotica, Hemihaplochromis multicolor, Haplochromis wingati* (all non-endemic), *Haplochromis mahagiensis, H. lanceolatus, H. avium, H. albertianus,* and *H. bullatus* (all endemic). See Regan (1921).

See Greenwood (1971) for descriptions of *H. loati* and important information on *H. wingati*.

LAKE EDWARD

South of Lake Albert is Lake Edward, and the two appear connected (probably with interruptions by rapids or falls) on my map by the Semliki River in the land of Ruwenzori. An important arthropod (mosquito) borne virus is known from this region. Lake Edward is 360 feet at its deepest, and 700 square miles in area (Greenwood, 1964). A smaller satellite lake to the northeast is Lake George, for which I have no data. Lake Edward has species in common with Lakes Victoria and Kivu, and their fish faunas appear to be derived from a common stem. The fishes of this lake include: *Tilapia nilotica, T. eduardiana, T. leucosticta, Schubotzia eduardiana, Haplochromis malacophagus, H. placodus, H. ishmaeli, H. macrops, H. pharyngalis, H. schubotzi, H. pappenheimi, H. nigripinnis, H. squamipinnis, H. vicarius, H. eduardi, H. elegans, H. guiarti, H. labiatus, H. augustifrons, H. serridens, H. limax,* and *H. fuscus.*

Limnotilapia dardennei

Haplochromis callipterus is one of the few members of its genus included among the rocky shore mbuna of Lake Malawi. Most Malawian *Haplochromis* species are included in the Utaka. Photo by Dr. R. J. Goldstein.

Hemitilapia oxyrhynchus. Photo by Michael K. Oliver.

Aulonocara macrochir, breeding male. Trawled from deep water. The enlarged head pores are visible. Photo by Michael K. Oliver.

LAKE KIVU

Lake Kivu is only 485 feet deep at its maximum (not deeper as I have previously published), and spills out into the Ruzizi River, which flows toward Lake Tanganyika. This smaller rift lake is stratified, with a saline layer below, making it quite different from other rift lakes. Lake Kivu is only some 15,000 years old. The deep water contains so much carbon dioxide and methane that it is only necessary to start drawing water up, and it will continue to gush like a geyser or self-driven air pump (Beauchamp, 1964). The small cichlid fauna consists of:
Tilapia nilotica, T. regani, Haplochromis paucidens, H. graueri, H. adolphifrederici, H. astatodon, H. vittatus, H. augustifrons, H. schoutedeni, H. burtoni, and *H. wittei.*

See also Poll (1932) and David and Poll (1937).

LAKE MALAWI

Lake Malawi is the southernmost of the Great Rift Lakes, extending from about 9°S to 14°S, at about 34°E. It covers an area of 11,000 square miles and has a maximum depth of about 2,600 feet. The "bush fire"-like swarms of insects seen over Lake Albert also occur here, as the offshore winds carry them out to "sea." Lake Malawi (previously called Lake Nyasa) is a deep cleft in the crust of the earth. The surface waters vary the year round from between 23.5 to 27.5°C, which is about room temperature. The very deep waters of the lake are only insignificantly cooler, and the temperature differential is insufficient to cause any kind of turnover. These deep and stagnant waters contain insufficient oxygen to sustain fish life.

The lake receives most of its water from prolonged nighttime thunderstorms, which appear due to the heat change of the land. Much of the surrounding land is arid and subject to great differentials in temperature over a 24-hour period. The bottom of the lake contains a deep layer of organic mud. Even though there is no annual turnover in Lake Malawi, there is some evidence of slight stratification. Beauchamp (1964) has suggested that Lake Malawi may "turn over" once every ten or twenty years, due to the action of very strong southeasterly winds. In the shallower parts of the lake, where the depth is not in excess of 1,000 feet, these winds may account for some annual turnover. In any case, whatever turnover occurs is accomplished by wind forces, rather than temperature differentials as is the case in temperate lakes. Because of the limited turnover in this lake, it is low in surface nutrients.

The total intake of water for Lake Malawi is 1,490 millimeters, 1,000 from rainfall and 490 from inflows. Evaporation loss is 1,300 millimeters. The lake is tenuously connected to the Zambezi River basin, and does have a fish fauna somewhat related to that of this river. The Zambezi's main body is south of the lake, and eventually empties into the Indian Ocean, at Barra Catarina, Mozambique. Loss of water to the Zambezi is insignificant, and there is some gain from smaller streams surrounding the lake, penetrating the arid land mass.

There are about 200 species of cichlids in Lake Malawi, in about 23 genera, and the vast majority of species and genera are endemic. There are only about 52 species of all other kinds of fishes in the lake, making the cichlid fishes the dominant family.

The first major collection at the lake was that of Sir John Kirk in the nineteenth century; these fishes were subsequently described by Albert Günther, in 1864. Twenty-nine years later Günther described an additional lot of fishes collected by Sir Harry Johnson. In the early part of the 20th century Boulenger, between 1908 and 1915, described a large number of cichlids collected by Captain Rhodes. Boulenger's (1915) *Catalogue of the Fresh-water Fishes of Africa* is still of tremendous value for his excellent illustrations, even though many of the names are no longer in use.

The first big treatise of the fishes of Lake Malawi was produced by C. Tate Regan in 1921. Regan coined very many of the generic names still in use today. Regan's material was collected by Rodney Wood, and deposited in the British Museum. Another collection was assembled in 1925 and 1926 by Dr. Cuthbert Christy, and Regan began work on this collection, but never finished it. The Christy collection consisted of about 4,300 fishes, of which 3,500 were cichlids. Dr. Ethelwyn Trewavas took up Regan's work and published her synopsis of the fishes of the lake in 1935. During the 1950s Dr. Geoffrey Fryer studied the ecology of the lake, including some of the fishes, and most cichlidophiles are familiar

Tylochromis lateralis. Photo by Hilmar Hansen, Aquarium Berlin.

Tylochromis lateralis. Photo by Dr. Herbert R. Axelrod.

with his 1959 ecological study of the mbuna, a group of rocky shore *Haplochromis*-derivatives. These are the fishes today known as the "Lake Nyasa cichlids," but they constitute only a small part of the cichlid fauna of this lake.

Another group, consisting of offshore *Haplochromis*, is known as the Utaka, and these may be imported in the very near future. In general, however, it is the rocky shore mbuna (a native name) that are the most vividly colored and striking fishes of this lake.

Tylochromis sp. Photo by Hilmar Hansen, Aquarium Berlin.

Lake Malawi is rather alkaline, but not especially hard or saline. Nonetheless, aquarists have had great success with these fishes by giving them hard, alkaline, somewhat saline conditions. Early imports consisted of the most common fishes of the rocky shores, including various color forms of *Pseudotropheus tropheops*, *P. auratus*, and various color forms of *P. zebra*, ranging from blue with dark bands to mottled to cobalt blue. Soon thereafter came in the two known sibling species of *Labeotropheus*, *L. trewavasae* and *L. fuelleborni*, but these fishes do not ship very well. *Pseudotropheus elongatus* was imported at about this time, and proved to be one of the most beautiful, but about the nastiest, cichlid yet imported. Also early in the importations was a brownish rust colored fish with a lavender sheen and occasional lateral barring. This fish came in under the name *Petrotilapia tridentiger*. Some time later it was found that this fish, although resembling shallow water *P. tridentiger* in color, was actually an undescribed species either fitting the generic definition of *Melanochromis*, or requiring a new generic heading. Because *Melanochromis* itself may be revised, the latter alternative was chosen and the fish is now known as *Iodotropheus sprengerae* Oliver and Loiselle, 1972, honoring Kappy Sprenger.

Recently additional species have come in, including *Haplochromis fenestratus*, *H.* sp. (so far unnamed and undescribed), *P. microstoma* and a host of other species of *Pseudotropheus*. A deep water form of *Petrotilapia tridentiger* has also been imported, and it in no way resembles the rust-colored shallow water form in color or markings.

Various species of the mbuna, in several genera, have variously colored males and either one female form or an additional female form characterized by extensive mottling with or without orange pigment.

As expected, in that they are all *Haplochromis* derivatives, is the observation that all of the mbuna are maternal mouthbrooders. The male guards a territory and breeds with any females that enter and are willing to spawn. During spawning the male's nuptial coloration usually intensifies (*Pseudotropheus zebra*), but may not if sexual dichromatism is already well-marked (*P. auratus*). The male swims out to meet the female and displays with extension of the fins (*P. zebra*) or some clamping of the fins (other species), but there is always a rapid darting back and forth which tends to excite her. The female at this time is usually heavy with roe and stored body nutrients (probably fat, but possibly protein as well), and may display the tip of her ovipositor as a slight nipple.

This is never as marked as the extension of the ovipositor in typical substratum brooders. Both fish make passes over the bottom, the female depositing large, generally yellow-white oval eggs, and the male sprays the area with milt as he too passes over the spawning site. The female snaps up the eggs rapidly and, at the conclusion of spawning, runs away to incubate the eggs in her throat pouch for three to five weeks. A few days before the well-developed fry are ready for release, she hunts for tight corners in which to release them, and tends to assume a muddy coloration. The fry are released a few at a time, sometimes over a period of a couple of days. During the whole time the female tends to reject food, and this is the best way of telling, in the aquarium, that a spawning has occurred, especially in those species which have small spawns resulting in a hardly distended throat pouch.

Macropleurodus bicolor, male, from Lake Victoria. Photo by Paul V. Loiselle.

Cyphotilapia frontosa, from Lake Tanganyika, has a prominant frontal region on the head. Photo by Hilmar Hansen, Aquarium Berlin.

Telmatochromis caninus of Lake Tanganyika. The fish has its branchiostegals expanded to warn intruders away from its territory.

Limnochromis otostigma is a commonly imported Tanganyikan cichlid, apparently not yet bred in captivity. Dr. Herbert R. Axelrod.

Limnochromis auritis from Lake Tanganyika is now commonly available, but at this writing no spawning reports were known. Photo by Dr. R. J. Goldstein.

When the fry are released they are already well developed and large, and the female should be removed to a recovery aquarium by herself, where she should be given good foods for at least one week (two are better) before returning her to her community tank. When removing her from the fry tank, use your fingers to press gently against the throat pouch, thereby forcing out (under water of course) any remaining fry. The same pressing method, if you prefer, can be used on females with a tendency to terminate incubation for unknown reasons. The eggs can be taken from the female and suspended in a net for artificial incubation with aeration, methylene blue or acriflavine, and filtered water from the breeding community tank. Suspension in a net is important to get the eggs jiggled around. The eggs are nonadhesive and must at all times have waste gases driven away or they will die.

Breeding the mbuna is best accomplished in a community tank with extensive rockwork. The larger the tank, the better it will be. The fish can also be set up as pairs, but here there is danger that an unready female may be damaged by an over-amorous male. It is usually best to let the female take care of the incubation in her throat pouch for the normal term, but the pressing method with artificial incubation is recommended for problem females (often species of *Labeotropheus*) with a tendency to spit out the eggs early and ignore them. Dirty or stagnant water will kill the eggs inside or outside the female's throat pouch. Always be sure the water is alkaline and spotlessly clean.

The fry will take newly hatched brine shrimp upon release or absorption of the yolk sac. The adult fishes should be given a varied diet, including some plant material. Many of them are herbivorous in nature, but adapt well to a very meaty diet in the aquarium. There is a suspicion that high plant material in the diet may be responsible for getting the best colors out of certain fishes, such as *Labeotropheus trewavasae*, the best males of which have a red dorsal fin.

Pseudotropheus auratus and *P. tropheops* have crossed in aquaria, yielding fertile hybrids which in turn produced offspring. Apparently these fishes do not hybridize in nature at all.

The evolution of the Lake Malawi fishes has prompted considerable discussion and debate among ichthyologists and other evolutionary biologists. Fryer pointed out that schooling behavior in some of the Lake Malawi forms might be regarded as the perpetuation of a juvenile character. It is well-known that very young cichlids of many (if not all) kinds maintain proximity to one another in the form of a shoal or school, and that they orient toward one or both parents. Eventually this orientation breaks down, and the shoal, in most species, also breaks down. Myers (1960) debated several of Fryer's points, pointing out areas of Fryer's presentation where alternative answers were just as logical, and problems in the acceptance of other aspects of Fryer's thesis. But all have applauded Fryer's presentation as refreshing and innovative, and likely to lead to a better understanding of the ecology of lake fishes. The American edition of his work was published (1972) by T.F.H. Publications under the title *The Cichlid Fishes of the Great Lakes of Africa.*

The fish fauna of Lake Malawi probably had its origins in the Zambezi River system, which has also affected the fish fauna in southern Africa. The Zambezi is a poorly known river, in terms of its diversity of species, its great number of species, and the specializations to be found in the various streams of the Zambezi basin. Myers (1960) has called for an intensive effort to be made on the fishes of this system.

Labeotropheus trewavasae male. Photo by Hilmar Hansen, Aquarium Berlin.

Melanochromis vermivorus (above and below) seems to vary slightly in head shape, and males resemble males of one or two other species of Lake Malawi. Photos by Hilmar Hansen, Aquarium Berlin.

Iodotropheus sprengerae, previously known as the rust or lavender cichlid, and as the ex-*tridentiger*. Photo by Dr. R. J. Goldstein.

This is a female of *Melanochromis vermivorus*. For some reason, few females of this species have been imported, resulting in very limited supplies of domestically bred specimens. Photo by G. Marcuse.

SOME CICHLIDS OF LAKE MALAWI

Aristochromis christyi
Aulonocara macrochir
A. nyassae
A. rostrata
Chilotilapia rhodesii
Corymatodus shiranus
C. taeniatus
Cyathochromis obliquidens
Cynotilapia afra
Diplotaxodon argenteus
Docimodus johnstoni
Genyochromis mento
Gephyrochromis lawsi
G. moorii
*Haplochromis (112 species)**
Hemitilapia oxyrhynchus
Labeotropheus fuelleborni
L. trewavasae
Labidochromis caeruleus
L. vellicans
Lethrinops brevis
L. furcifer
L. praeorbitalis
L. laticeps
L. (20 other species)
Lichnochromis acuticeps
Melanochromis brevis
M. labrosus
M. melanopterus
M. perspicax
M. vermivorus
Petrotilapia tridentiger
Pseudotropheus auratus
P. elegans
P. elongatus
P. fuscoides
P. fuscus
P. livingstonii
P. lucerna
P. microstoma
P. minutus
P. novemfasciatus
P. tropheops
P. williamsi
P. zebra
Rhamphochromis longiceps
R. macrophthalmus
R. brevis
R. woodii
R. fero
R. lucius
R. esox
R. leptosoma
Serranochromis robustus
Tilapia saka
T. squamipinnis
T. melanopleura
T. shirana
T. kirongae
Trematocranus auditor
T. brevirostris
T. microstoma

* See the partial list of *Haplochromis* species in the next table.

PARTIAL LIST OF THE 112 OR MORE *HAPLOCHROMIS* OF LAKE MALAWI

lobochilotes
euchilus
mola
placodon
incola
rostratus
compressiceps
moorii
virginalis
quadrimaculatus
pleurostigmoides
similis
johnstoni
callipterus
fenestratus
ornatus
pardalis
polyodon
kiwinge
guentheri
dimidiatus
chrysonotus
venustus
polystigma
obliquidens
livingstoni
oromarginatus
selenurus
annectens
nkatae

LAKE TANGANYIKA

Lake Tanganyika, also spelled Tanganyka, is one of the Great Rift Valley lakes of East Africa. In depth it is second only to Asia's Lake Baikal, extending downward to over 4000 feet in places. Most of its deep offshore waters are only 2000 feet deep! Extending from north to south for about 400 miles, and from east to west some fifty miles, it covers an area about 12,700 square miles, or an area equal to the entire country of Belgium. The elevation of the surrounding countryside is 2500 feet on the average, and mountains rise up around the eastern and western rims of the Great Rift Valley.

The southern shore is the country of Zambia; to the east is Tanzania; to the west is The Congo; and in the northeast is Burundi. We should note at once that all the Lake Tanganyika fishes coming in at the present time are from the Burundi part of the lake front, for here is where Pierre Brichard has set up his massive collecting station. Since this is one point only in an area that extends 400 miles farther southward, we must expect that certain (probably many) species of the lake will not be found in Brichard's area of activity.

A number of rivers connect with Lake Tanganyika, but the most important of them is the Congo River, whose drainage basin contains a fish fauna closely allied to Lake Tanganyika. Recall, if you will, the similarity of the two systems. *Lamprologus mocquardi* comes from the Congo River, and Lake Tanganyika contains many species of *Lamprologus*. (This is in contrast to

Petrotilapia tridentiger, deep-water form from Lake Malawi. The yellow individual is a female and the other two are males, illustrating pattern variation. Note the large, fleshy lips. Photo by Dr. R. J. Goldstein.

Tropheus moorii from Lake Tanganyika. Usually found in rocky habitat. Photo by Dr. Herbert R. Axelrod.

Tropheus duboisi, juvenile, from Lake Tanganyika. Photo by Peter Chlupaty.

Lake Malawi, where the major river system influencing its fauna is the Zambezi.) The connection with the Congo has been disrupted, and now only a large floodplain-like swampy area remains. Perhaps in the future there will be sufficiently heavy rains in the region to set up another transitory connection.

To the north of the lake is the relatively minor Ruzizi River. It arises from a flood plain of Lake Kivu still farther northward.

In common with several other Rift Valley Lakes, there is no major seasonal turnover of nutrients. This is because of lack of a good temperature differential here near the equator, and the great depth of the lake, which is best illustrated as a deep slice in the earth's crust. This non-turnover condition makes the lake oligotrophic, containing little nutrient material. The surface waters average pH 9.0, and this high alkalinity suggests high concentrations of sodium and magnesium bicarbonates. The surface temperature averages 27°C, and you have to travel 400 meters down to drop to 23°C. Obviously, these fishes are not subject to much temperature fluctuation. The great depths of the lake are relatively anoxic and acidic. Much of the water in the lake gets there via heavy nighttime thunderstorms. I have no data on water hardness.

Perhaps the most lucid and concise description of this extraordinary lake that I have seen was written to me in a letter from Paul V. Loiselle, who visited Brichard's Burundi station in July of 1971. Paul writes:

> ". . . Burundi is a nice, if expensive, place for a vacation, and skindiving in the lake is unbelievable (no crocs or bilharzia if you stay away from river mouths). Underwater visibility is easily 200 feet, and the rocky areas are like coral reefs—solid cichlids. . . . Someone with an underwater camera would go bananas in that place."

The lake was discovered by the British explorers Burton and Speke in 1858, a year before Charles Darwin published *The Origin of Species and the Descent of Man.* Twenty years later the lake was revisited by Moore and Thomson. All four explorers noted the presence of strange molluscs, and to them this suggested the possibility that the lake arose as an arm of the sea; in fact Moore in 1903 published this hypothesis, and assumed that this sea arm became a lake in Jurassic times. At about the same time the great ichthyologist Boulenger noticed the great similarity between

Lake Tanganyika fishes and those of the Congo and other African rivers; he pointed out that the fishes resembled freshwater fishes far more than marine forms, and this indicated that the presence of molluscs must have some other explanation than a marine origin.

There are about 134 species of cichlids in 34 genera, and practically all the species (and almost all the genera) are endemic, i.e., occurring here and no place else. Of the four species of *Tilapia*, two are endemic and the others have probably been somehow introduced. *T. rendalli* and *T. nilotica* are widespread in Africa. *T. karomo* occurs in the lower Malagarazi and associated swamps, and occupies swamplike portions of Lake Tanganyika.

There are only four species of *Haplochromis* in the lake (recall the numbers in lakes Victoria and Malawi) and a single species of the closely related *Orthochromis*. These five fishes mainly occupy tributary streams of the lake, with three of them getting into the shoreline parts of the lake itself. *H. horei* is the most lake-like one of the group. And so it is these *Haplochromis*/*Orthochromis* river-like groups on the one hand, and the *Tilapia* group on the other hand (also mainly riverine fishes) constituting the fluvial (river)

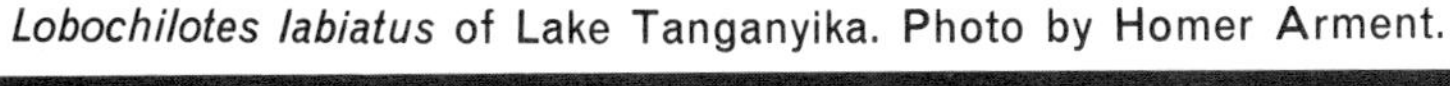
Lobochilotes labiatus of Lake Tanganyika. Photo by Homer Arment.

types. All the others not closely related are mainly considered lacustrine (lake-type), and only rarely get into the rivers. Of course there is an exception to this nice generalization and it is *Lamprologus stappersii*, which is found *solely* in rivers! Poll divides the cichlids into three or four ecological groups, as follows:

Rocky Shores

There are many and diverse rocky shores to this lake, and they do not make up a single area only. Due to heavy wave action,

Julidochromis marlieri, a bottom nester from Lake Tanganyika, and probably the largest species of its genus. Photo by Dr. R. J. Goldstein.

Julidochromis ornatus, a small member of its genus. The julies are inhabitants only of Lake Tanganyika, and are easily bred. Photo by H. J. Richter.

there is no vegetation among the rocks of the shore, but where the rocks extend into the water they may be covered with much algae. Of course, many kinds of crustaceans and insect larvae associate with the algae. Typical rocky shore cichlids include: *Limnotilapia dardennei, L. loocki, Lobochilotes, Aulonocranus, Simochromis, Petrochromis, Cyathopharynx, Cunningtonia, Tropheus moorii, Limnochromis pfefferi, Ophthalmochromis ventralis, Ophthalmotilapia, Eretmodus, Spathodus, Tanganicodus, Telmatochromis, Julidochromis,* and about 20 species of *Lamprologus*, most commonly *L. tetracanthus, L. elongatus,* and *L. modestus.*

In the rather deep rocky bottoms (extending out from the beach even farther), other species now can be found: *Cyphotilapia frontosa, Haplotaxodon microlepis,* a number of *Lamprologus* including *elongatus* (a big one), *attenuatus,* and *profundicola.*

The rocky shore fishes are generally more colorful than sand bottom fishes. They remain among the rocks, and feed actively toward dusk (and probably also in the mornings). *Limnotilapia* and *Petrochromis* feed largely on algae, while many of the others eat insect larvae, crustacea and other fishes (*Lamprologus*). Most of them eat worms or other meaty diets.

Sandy Shores

This type of shoreline is not as common as the rocky shore, and most sandy shores occur to the east on the Tanzanian coast. Some beaches are sand or gravel, while others have developed sandstone formations useful in estimating the earlier rises and falls in the lake level during its evolution. The water here is rougher, and more brightly lit by the sun, and the fishes cannot go into rocks to get out of the glare. Thus, the fish do not occur close to the beach but somewhat out under the waves where the water is quieter. The fishes of this type of habitat are uniformly drab, either silvery or dull yellow-olive with darker smudges. Typical genera are *Lestradea, Cardiopharynx, Callochromis, Xenotilapia, Ectodus, Grammatotria, Tylochromis,* and *Tilapia tanganicae,* normally a plankton feeder of rivers. Except for this one species, all the others are probably bottom feeders on small organisms. *Tylochromis* feeds mostly on snails. There is no vegetation here to eat. At night other fishes from the muddy bottoms enter this area to feed.

The Benthic Habitat

The very deep parts of the lake are not capable of supporting fish life, but the vast regions down to about 200 meters do have fishes. Poll notes that this is about the level of the continental shelves of the marine habitats. The benthos is characterized by various kinds of bottoms, but mud bottoms are common. Light is decreased in the depths, and at 120 meters the oxygen concentration is only a tenth of that at the surface. The fishes of the benthos are bottom-types, rather than open water types. The most numerous fishes are *Trematocara*, then *Xenotilapia*, then eleven kinds of *Limnochromis*, seven *Bathybates*, and four *Plecodus*. Other benthic species are *Boulengerochromis* (a ferocious predator and the largest cichlid known), *Leptochromis*, *Hemibates*, *Haplotaxodon*, *Xenochromis*, and several *Lamprologus*. Most of the benthic fishes are found in 120 meters of water or less, and the greatest number occur in the southern part of the lake rather than the warmer northern part, a fact which Poll attributes to the greater oxygen saturation.

The critical depth increases from north to south, and in the warmer northern part of the lake the fishes disappear at about 120 meters, while in the south they may occur up to 200 meters deep.

Bathypelagic Cichlids

These are cichlids which follow the plankton down during the day and upward at night. (You really have to "think marine" when considering this lake, as its vast size lends it to many of the same environmental situations associated with the sea rather than with a freshwater habitat.) These bathypelagic fishes are not adapted to resting on the bottom. Their pelvic fins are normal, with the first rays short; the bottom resting forms have the first rays elongated (typically). Typical bathypelagic forms are *Limnochromis*, *Trematocara*, and young *Xenochromis* and *Haplotaxodon*. All of the above feed largely on copepods and small crustaceans. The remaining bathypelagic forms eat things larger than plankton! *Bathybates*, *Hemibates*, *Plecodus* and *Perissodus* eat small herring-like fishes (especially the first two genera), while the latter two genera have the nasty habit of ripping the scales and skin off other fishes.

Pseudotropheus novemfasciatus of Lake Malawi. Photo by Klaus Paysan.

Pseudotropheus elongatus of Lake Malawi cannot be confused with anything else. It is one of the roughest species in its genus. Photo by D. Terver at Nancy Aquarium, France.

Pseudotropheus microstoma from Lake Malawi, female. Photo by Dr. R. J. Goldstein.

Pseudotropheus microstoma from Lake Malawi, male. Photo by Dr. R. J. Goldstein.

REPRODUCTIVE BEHAVIOR

The following species are now known to be mouthbrooders: *Tylochromis*, *Tilapia tanganicae*, *Limnotilapia dardennei*, *Simochromis diagramma*, *Tropheus moorii*, *Petrochromis polyodon*, *Lestradea*, *Cardiopharynx*, *Cyathopharynx*, *Limnochromis pfefferi*, *Haplochromis burtoni*, *H. horei*, *Ectodus*, *Callochromis*, *Grammatotria*, *Xenotilapia*, *Aulonocranus*, *Trematocara* (four species), *Bathybates ferox* and *Tanganicodus irsacae*. Apparently all of the *Lamprologus*, *Julidochromis* and *Telmatochromis* are substratum brooders. As you see, we have a lot of gaps.

It must be emphasized that the species flocks of Lake Tanganyika are rather different from the flock of Lake Malawi. The latter clearly contains fishes related to a *Haplochromis*-like ancestor, and this group has often been called "the *Haplochromis* species flock." The situation in Lake Tanganyika is otherwise. Although only a few *Haplochromis* species occur there, and there is a great preponderance of endemic genera, it appears that the fishes of this lake were derived from both *Tilapia* and *Haplochromis* types of ancestors. Thus, at least two species flocks occur in Lake Tanganyika, and the evolution of these groups is far more obscure than is the case in Lake Malawi. *Tylochromis* represents an independent line.

The social behavior and spawning of *Tropheus moorii* was presented by Wickler (1969) and others. In these maternal mouthbrooders, only about four to six (but up to ten) eggs are produced, and the incubation period is about a month, as with other Rift Lake mouthbrooders. There is little or no sexual dichromatism and no dimorphism. The eggs are about seven millimeters in length, and this large size accounts for the relatively small spawns. Apparently *T. moorii* has been spawned a number of times in Germany, and they have only recently been imported into the U.S.A., where propagation can be expected. *T. moorii* is a shallow water fish of the rocky shores. *T. duboisi* occurs in deeper water, and thus is not as readily accessible to collectors at the lake. It is rare in the hobby at present.

A number of authors have reported breeding *Julidochromis ornatus*, one of the most widespread Tanganyika cichlids in the hobby. This yellow and black beauty, somewhat resembling a small, streamlined version of Lake Malawi's *Pseudotropheus auratus*, is not dichromatic. Females tend to be much larger than males. "Julies" are substratum brooders and spawns are not large. The fry are quite secretive.

Julies are probably among the most attractive of the Lake Tanganyika cichlids. Other species in the hobby include *J. marlieri*, with a checkerboard pattern of brown on white, with iridescent blue highlights to the fin edges, and an unnamed species of julie being bred in South Africa, characterized by much white coloration below. *J. marlieri* attains about four inches, while *J. ornatus* remains about half that size. *J. regani* is a horizontally striped fish, and may not yet be known in the hobby.

Lamprologus compressiceps resembles a leaf fish in appearance and habits. Apparently little is known of its breeding. *Lamprologus savoryi elongatus* has recently been imported in large numbers, and is available at relatively low prices. This is a modestly colored fish, whose claim to fame is in its graceful lines and manners. *L. modestus* has been spawned recently, and as with other species of its genus, is a typical substratum brooder (see Pierce and Pierce, 1971). Females apparently larger than males, but this is based on one report only.

The genus *Telmatochromis* is closely related to *Lamprologus*. One species is commonly available and inexpensive, and this is *T. temporalis*. Males larger than females, the latter breeding at two inches, the former at one and a half. Eggs are average sized, opaque white, and number about fifty per spawn. Fry secretive, and with a tendency to stay on the bottom motionlessly, only hopping about to obtain food. Growth is slow.

Lake Tanganyika cichlids do well in hard, alkaline water with a great deal of rockwork and some gravel or sand. Some of them tend to hang vertically or upside down along or beneath rocks. Aquarists generally give each species a tank of its own. Substratum brooders are belligerent, while mouthbrooders seem to handle much like the Lake Malawi mbuna. The prices of these fishes are dropping rapidly, with the great numbers being shipped in from Pierre Brichard's station at Burundi. Most do well on small, living foods. It is important to keep their water alkaline and cool. The major taxonomic papers are those by Poll. See the bibliography for references.

Lake Malawi's mbuna complex of *Haplochromis*-derivatives are also mouthbrooders. Shown here are the male (above) and incubating female of *Pseudotropheus auratus*. Photos by D. Terver, Nancy Aquarium, France.

Pseudotropheus tropheops, the orange form. Photo by Dr. Herbert R. Axelrod.

Pseudotropheus tropheops, yellow form.

Pseudotropheus tropheops, endemic species of Lake Malawi. Typical form. Photo by D. Terver, Nancy Aquarium, France.

LAKE TANGANYIKA CICHLIDS

Asprotilapia leptura
Aulonocranus dewindti
Bathybates fasciatus
B. ferrox
B. graueri
B. horni
B. leo
B. minor
Boulengerochromis microlepis
Callochromis macrops
C. pleurospilus
Cardiopharynx schoutedeni
Cunningtonia longiventralis
Cyathopharynx furcifer
Cyphotilapia frontosa
Ectodus descampsii
Enantiopus boulengeri
Eretmodus cyanostictus
Grammatotria lemairii
Gephyrochromis moorii
Haplochromis burtoni
H. horei
H. straeleni
H. stappersii
Haplotaxodon microlepis
H. tricoti
Hemibates stenosoma
Julidochromis marlieri
J. ornatus
J. regani
J. transcriptus
Lamprologus fasciatus
L. attenuatus
L. christyi
L. ocellatus
L. pleuromaculatus
L. sexfasciatus
L. signatus
L. compressiceps
L. cunningtoni
L. leleupi
L. leloupi
L. moorii
L. modestus
L. elongatus
L. furcifer
L. lemairii
L. hecqui
L. brevis
L. tretocephalus
L. tetracanthus
L. mondabu
L. multifasciatus
L. callipterus
L. pleurostigma
L. stappersii
L. macrolepis
L. lestradei
L. meeli
L. profundicola
L. petricola
L. toae
L. savoryi
L. wauthioni
L. ornatipinnis
Leptochromis calliura
Lestradea perspicax
Limnochromis abeelei
L. auritis
L. dhanisi

L. microlepidotus
L. otostigma
L. permaxillaris
L. pfefferi
L. staneri
Limnotilapia dardennei
L. loocki
L. pleurotaenia
L. trematocephala
Lobochilotes labiatus
Ophthalmochromis stappersii
O. ventralis
Ophthalmotilapia boops
O. stappersii
Orthochromis malagaraziensis
Parectodus hemelrycki
P. lestradei
Perissodus burgeoni
P. gracilis
P. microlepis
Petrochromis fasciolatus
P. famula
P. orthognathus
P. trewavasae
P. polyodon
Plecodus elaviae
P. paradoxus
P. straeleni
P. multidentatus
Simochromis babaulti
S. diagramma
S. curvifrons
Spathodus erythrodon
S. marlieri
Tanganicodus irsacae
Telmatochromis bifrenatus
T. burgeoni
T. caninus
T. lestradei
T. temporalis
T. vittatus
Tilapia nilotica
T. rendalli
T. tanganicae
T. karomo
Trematocara unimaculatum
T. marginatum
T. nigrifrons
T. stigmaticum
T. caparti
T. kufferathi
T. macrostoma
T. variabile
Tropheus moorii
T. duboisi
Tylochromis polylepis
T. mylodon
T. lateralis
Xenochromis hecqui
X. ornatipinnis
X. materfamilias
Xenotilapia caudafasciata
X. longispinis
X. materfamilias
X. nigrolabiata
X. ochrogenys
X. tenuidentata
X. sima

Pseudotropheus zebra, mottled form. Mottled females of Rift Lake cichlids are well-known, but in *P. zebra* mottled males are known as well. Photo by Dr. Robert J. Goldstein.

Labeotropheus fuelleborni, the larger of the two species of this genus, endemic to Lake Malawi. Photo by D. Terver of the Nancy Aquarium.

Enlargement of a six-day post-release juvenile of *Labeotropheus fuelleborni*.

Labeotropheus trewavasae is smaller and more elongate than its cogener. The red color in the male's fins is variable, but usually better developed in wild fish. Females are typically mottled, but may be almost white, with some speckling. Photo by D. Terver, Nancy Aquarium, France.

LAKE VICTORIA

Lake Victoria, with an area of 26,000 square miles, is one of the largest of all the world's lakes. Located in a large, saucer-shaped depression between the overlapping northern and southern arms of the Great Rift Valley, it is not actually one of the rift lakes. The average depth is only 140 feet, and its maximal depth is a mere 270 feet. For a lake of its vast area, it is quite shallow. For details see Beauchamp (1964), Temple (1969), and Greenwood (1964). The major ichthyological papers are the numerous ones of Greenwood (see the bibliography). The fishes of this lake are virtually unknown to the hobby, but there are a few word-of-mouth reports regarding hand-carried imports. It is quite fortunate that many of Greenwood's papers give color descriptions of living fishes, and these will be a boon to aquarists once the myriad species of *Haplochromis* start to arrive in abundance.

For some time it was thought that Lake Victoria was very old, and that it had gone through at least one major period of desiccation. This would have explained the present day examples of fishes found in the fossils of the area, as well as the presence of newer and different kinds of fishes, thought to have been introduced when the lake refilled. But in a recent paper, Temple (1969) suggested that the lake is only as old as the mid-Pleistocene, which is far younger than previous estimates. The idea of a period of desiccation was shown to be probably untrue, and not necessary to explain the fossils. In earlier times, the entire plateau was tilted differently, and there were other distinct lakes in the area, lakes which were *not* ancestral to Lake Victoria. These older lakes were formed by volcanic damming. Eventually, geologic activity caused these lakes to break down. The whole region was later warped by further geologic activity, and *new* small lakes were formed.

These small lakes were drained westward, and some of their fishes found their way into Lake Edward. With further activity, the lakes began to fill up, their drainages interrupted. As they filled and rose, they eventually met and merged, to become Lake Victoria. Thus, the distinct fishes that had occurred in each lake now found themselves sharing one much larger lake. This resulted in several different groups of *Haplochromis*-type fishes finding their way into the new Lake Victoria, and subsequent evolution

Sedge shoreline at Jinja, Lake Victoria. Photo by Paul V. Loiselle.

has maintained and played with these distinct categories, but not to the extent that we can easily define myriad genera. The differences still seem to be at the species level, and generic divisions from *Haplochromis* are practically absent, only five monotypic genera recognized today (see the table). Thus, while Boulenger (1915) recognized only 47 species of cichlids in this lake, today we recognize about 130, and almost all of them belong in the genus *Haplochromis*.

There are four major trophic (feeding) types: the plant feeders, the insect feeders, the fish eaters, and the embryo snatchers. Members of this last group get much of their food by engulfing the snout of a brooding female mouthbrooder (apparently they are all maternal mouthbrooders) and forcing her to expel her eggs or fry into the mouth of the snatcher. How this is done is not clear, but probably it does not differ much from the way in which an aquarist can accomplish the same end, *i.e.*, by squeezing the lower portion of the brood pouch, popping upwards, and forcing the contents outward. The ease with which this is accomplished can be best seen on a preserved fish.

Seven species of cichlids from Lakes Malawi and Tanganyika are known to be scale-eaters. These are *Genyochromis mento*,

Labeotropheus trewavasae, an atypical strain. Photo by Dr. Herbert R. Axelrod.

Telmatochromis bifrenatus looks much like Lake Tanganyika's version of a species of *Crenicichla*. Photo by Paul V. Loiselle.

Corematodus shiranus, and *C. taeniatus* from Lake Malawi; and from Lake Tanganyika, *Perissodus microlepis* and three species of *Plecodus*. Only one scale-eater is known from Lake Victoria, and it is *Haplochromis welcommei*. As with the other scale-eaters, the scales are scraped from the upper sides or from the peduncle of other fishes, and do not make up the total diet. These fishes also eat fin ray segments, algae, and other plant materials. *H. welcommei* is described by Greenwood as having a bright red flush on the flanks, cheek and operculum, bright red streaks on the soft dorsal and on the caudal fin, and bright yellow ocelli on the anal fin. Nonetheless, it is unlikely that aquarists will ever popularize this fish because of its nasty habits.

Lake Victoria receives 1,260 millimeters of rainfall and another 330 millimeters from inflow. It loses 1,310 of this 1,590 total by evaporation. Because of its shallow nature, Lake Victoria does turn over annually, as do temperate lakes. Stratification occurs by cooling of the lower layers, and not by heating of the upper layers, as occurs in temperate lakes. As you can see, this large equatorial lake is subject to forces different from those that affect the large temperate lakes. Heavy storms and winds probably also contribute to the turnover. In the shallows of this lake are extensive deposits of greenish black mud, covering hundreds of square miles. The deepest parts of the lake are free of this mud, and tend to be sandy. The mud itself contains a very high concentration of a strange microorganism somewhere between the blue-green algae and the bacteria (Beauchamp, 1964). The mud does not decompose until after it has been boiled. It then turns putrid. Apparently this strange microorganism accounts for the unusual behavior of the mud, which is almost an organic matrix of materials.

The explosive speciation of the species of *Haplochromis* of Lake Victoria was discussed by Greenwood (1964), and that paper is required reading for all serious cichlidophiles. There are very few plant eaters, and the vast majority of the fishes are piscivorous. All appear to be maternal mouthbrooders, and the males of all species are very colorful and marked differently from the females. Most are about four inches in maximal length, and thus are small fishes, suitable for aquaria.

CICHLIDS OF LAKE VICTORIA

Astatoreochromis alluaudi
Hoplotilapia retrodens
Macropleurodus bicolor
Paralabidochromis victoriae
Platytaeniodus degeni
Tilapia esculenta
T. variabilis
T. zillii
T. nilotica
Haplochromis acidens
H. acutirostris
H. aelocephalus
H. annectens
H. argenteus
H. altigenis
H. apogonoides
H. arcanus
H. artaxerxes
H. barbarae
H. bartoni
H. bayoni
H. boops
H. brownae
H. cavifrons
H. chilotes
H. chlorochrous
H. chromogynos
H. cinctus
H. cinereus
H. crassilabris
H. cronus
H. cryptodon
H. cryptogramma
H. decticostoma
H. dentex
H. dichrourus

H. dolichorhynchus
H. empodisma
H. erythrocephalus
H. estor
H. flavipinnis
H. fusiformis
H. gestri
H. gilberti
H. gowersi
H. gracilicauda
H. granti
H. guiarti
H. humilior
H. ishmaeli
H. lacrimosus
H. laparogramma
H. lividus
H. longirostris
H. macrodon
H. macrognathus
H. macrops
H. maculipinna
H. mandibularis
H. martini
H. maxillaris
H. megalops
H. melanopterus
H. melanopus
H. melichrous
H. mento
H. michaeli
H. microdon
H. nigrescens
H. nigricans
H. niloticus
H. nuchisquamulatus
H. nubilus
H. nyanzae
H. obesus
H. obliquidens
H. obtusidens
H. orthostoma
H. pachycephalus
H. pallidus
H. paraguiarti
H. paraplagiostoma
H. paropius
H. parorthostoma
H. parvidens
H. pellegrini
H. percoides
H. pharyngomylus
H. phytophagus
H. piceatus
H. plagiodon
H. plagiostoma
H. prodromus
H. prognathus
H. pseudopellegrini
H. riponianus
H. sauvagei
H. saxicola
H. serranus
H. serranoides
H. spekii
H. squamulatus
H. taeniatus
H. theliodon
H. thuragnathus
H. tridens
H. tyrianthinus
H. victorianus
H. welcommei
H. wingatei
H. xenodon
H. xenognathus
H. xenostoma

CICHLIDS OF MADAGASCAR

The Malagasy Republic occupies the entire island of Madagascar, which lies in the Indian Ocean, separated from the coast of Southeast Africa by the Mozambique Channel. A number of species and genera of cichlids are endemic to this tropical island. Recently, Kiener and Maugé (1966) reviewed the cichlids of the island.

The largest genus is *Paretroplus,* with five species; *P. dami, P. polyactis, P. maculatus, P. petiti,* and *P. kieneri.* These are generally deep-bodied fishes with small heads, superficially resembling *Etroplus,* or *Cichlasoma centrarchus. P. maculatus* has a large dark blotch above and behind the pectoral fin. *P. polyactis* has short bars along the upper part of the sides. *P. dami* has a rather enlarged snout area.

Paratilapia polleni is a darkly beautiful fish, with well developed finnage, and Jack Dempsey front profile. It is covered with light spots set in startling contrast.

Ptychochromis oligacanthus is another pretty species, which exists as different geographic races along the island. They may be dark, light, or intermediate with a series of three or four large blotches. The general coloration is blue-gray to red-brown. The dorsal may be violet, edged in dark red. The caudal and anal may be dark red. The most colorful form is from the area of Mandritsara, in the interior north of the island. The less colorful forms are coastal.

Oxylapia polli is an elongate fish with a dark blotch at the upper angle of the gill cover. It is not an attractively colored species, but its shape makes it easy to identify if you know that it's from Madagascar.

Ptychochromoides betsileanus is generally sunfish shaped, but it has a very enlarged lump on its forehead, almost (but not quite) as impressive as in the lumphead, *Steatocranus,* from the Congo. It even more closely resembles the African species, *Cyphotilapia frontosa* from Lake Tanganyika.

Tilapia melanopleura and *T. mossambica* have been introduced and established on the island.

Cyphotilapia frontosa of Lake Tanganyika. Photo by Gerhard Budich.

Apparently none of these native fishes has yet been introduced to the hobby, at least in the United States. And so we have something else for cichlidophiles to look forward to. Notice the absence of *Haplochromis* and native *Tilapia* from the island.

Madagascar is a mountainous land, rising out of a 12,000 foot sea bed. Due west, from the north of the island, are the famous Comoro Islands, home of that Devonian relic, the coelacanth.

Nomenclature

Before stating how species are named, it would be a good idea to define the term *species*. I'm afraid I can't do it, and don't know anyone else who can. There are several reasons for this, and the basis for the confusion might be laid by pointing out one fact: *A species in the legal zoological sense is different from a species in the purely biological sense.* This means that a legal species is defined as the individual or group of individuals which are deposited in a museum under the particular species name. It is immediately apparent that something can be legally correct but biologically wrong! How can this be? Because, legally, the group (if it is a group) in the museum can in no way reflect the total variation inherent in a natural population.

Suppose there are five (or even fifty) specimens of *Cichlasoma whatzit* in a museum. The population in nature, from which this group was taken, may number a million. Surely, from our museum group we have only an inkling, at best, of what any individual in nature may look like! For the *biological species* is the *whole* population of animals during a given span of time, and that population is as variable as man, canaries, brook trout, or anything else. The great ichthyologist, George S. Myers, pointed out in 1960, and before, that all persons concerned with schemes for illustrating the descent or limits of species are limited by not knowing either the total variation of a population, or even knowing the biology, thoroughly, of a single member of that population. For it is not merely fin ray numbers that evolve, but blood chemistry, innervation, organ and enzyme activities, and every part and function of an animal that is concerned with the nature of the biological species! Taxonomists, on the other hand, study only parts of animals, and study only small samples of animals. Thus, taxonomy is in large part educated guesswork at the level of phylogenetic relationships. Hopefully, the guesswork is based on enough of the picture to be *probably* correct. But we don't know this for sure, and we can never know it. Did all modern *Cichlasoma* arise from a common ancestor? We don't know. Perhaps this genus had a multiple origin. But it's the best way we

Cichlasoma spilotum is a large, yet gentle, fish from Costa Rica, with a rich golden-green flush to its body. Photo by Paul V. Loiselle.

have, today, to show the relationships of the fishes now in that group, as we understand them. Does *Symphysodon* contain one, two or more species? Again, we don't know. Legally, there are two species. Biologically . . . who knows?

Now that you are sufficiently depressed, and have decided that you will never be a taxonomist, we can move on to how species are named. (Parenthetically, I hope some of you are stimulated and challenged rather than depressed. If you are, then you are the stuff from which progress grows.)

Species are named in accordance (and sometimes despite) a set of principles embodied (largely, but not entirely) in the *International Code of Zoological Nomenclature*. These rules were agreed upon by different Commissions on Zoological Nomenclature. The rules didn't attain their present form all at once, but are the result of different commissions convening at different times and discussing all kinds of apparent exceptions and challenges. And the standing commissions have ruled on specific cases (often with far-reaching implications) during periods when they were not formally all sitting down together. It is very much like law.

Now suppose you have just come back from a collecting trip to a place that nobody has previously studied. Your jars are filled with pickled fishes, and each jar is labeled with the precise locality, date, and even time of the day (for some occasionally useful reason). In going through all your goodies, you come upon a fish that resembles a known species, but somehow it seems different. Picking up your calipers and ruler, you measure the total and standard lengths of several of them. Then you make other measurements. With a magnifying glass and a probe, you carefully count the fin rays and the scales along the lateral line and around the body just before the pelvic fins (or elsewhere), and you determine the number of scale rows between the dorsal fin and upper lateral line, etc. You examine the teeth and a series of other characteristics, all of which do or might have something to do with the characters used to classify members of this particular group of fishes. You note its coloration in the pickling fluid, and refer to your notes for its color in life. You stay with the job until you have measured the population of fish sixteen ways from

Limnochromis auritis of Lake Tanganyika. Photo by Homer Arment.

Sunday, and cannot find another blessed characteristic to measure or otherwise record. You do the same on museum collections of similar or related fishes.

The next step is to compare your notes and data with everything published on this and related groups in the past. It is not enough for you to be convinced that you have a unique, never-before-recorded species. You have to present sufficient data to convince others of the same idea. A number of ichthyologists will send copies of their ideas and data to others competent in the field before preparing a manuscript for publication. And so, let us assume that this has been done (or the fish is so unique that it need not be done), and we are ready to write the manuscript.

The manuscript is carefully prepared, presenting an introduction to the fish (or the problem) and a bit on the status of this group of fishes as it is known today. You must review all relevant literature. You then go on to propose a name for the new fish, and follow this with a detailed description that (hopefully) will enable persons a hundred years from now to recognize your fish in the field or from a pickled specimen in such detail that there should be no chance of ever confusing this fish with anything else. Of course, sometimes this fails because a fish is subsequently discovered that shares most or all of the characters you have covered, but differs in one or more significant characters you have not covered, and the significance is only apparent in retrospect. Many of the very early species descriptions were brief or general, and subsequent discoveries have forced re-evaluations of which names should be applied to different fishes (or sometimes the same fish). If you simply propose a name and do not present an adequate description, this name becomes a *nomen nudum* (meaning: a naked name, or a name without a description) and is invalid. It has no standing and should not be subsequently used. There are many cases of *nomina nuda* (the plural) in the cichlid literature.

You choose a recognized scholarly journal, and send two or three copies of your manuscript, plates, drawings, tables, etc., to the editor. He will acknowledge receipt and then send the copies to other scholars in the same field who function as referees. The referees will carefully evaluate the material, make useful suggestions on how the manuscript might be improved, or whether the author is way off base by, perhaps, missing another pertinent paper. The referees will then either approve, disapprove, or approve with recommendations for changes. The referees and the editor will also comment on how the same things might be said in fewer words, or with less ambiguity. Let us assume that they all agree to publish the paper. Upon publication in the journal, and not before, the name becomes a published name, and its legality (validity) is assumed unless subsequently challenged. A challenge to the validity of a name must go through pretty much the same procedures.

The referee system is not required by the rules, but it is almost universally used among scientific journals, whatever the discipline. Any journal that fails to use this system generally has a poor reputation in the ichthyological community and few reputable authors will publish therein.

Manuscripts are generally written following the guidelines published by the American Institute of Biological Sciences (AIBS). The book is called the STYLE MANUAL FOR BIOLOGICAL JOURNALS, and may be purchased from the AIBS, 2000 P Street, NW, Washington, D.C. 20036, USA.

Cichlasoma salvini from British Honduras is a very beautiful and rather recent addition to the hobby. Photo by Dr. R. J. Goldstein.

The philosophy of good scientific writing is perhaps best expressed in the following little ditty that I learned as a graduate student. I have not been able to trace the original author, but it was most likely an editor of the *Journal of Parasitology*. And since all zoologists (whether parasitologists or ichthyologists) follow the same rules and guidelines of zoological nomenclature, the relevance is universal.

BOIL IT DOWN
(Anonymous)

If you've got a thought that's happy, boil it down.
Make it short and crisp and snappy. Boil it down.
When your brain its coin has minted,
Down the page your pen has sprinted,
If you want your effort printed, boil it down.

Take out every surplus letter. Boil it down.
Fewer syllables the better. Boil it down.
Make your meaning plain; express it so
we'll know, not merely guess it.
Then my friend, ere you address it, boil it down.

Skim it well, then skim the skimmings. Boil it down.
Trim it, then retrim the trimmings. Boil it down.
When you're sure 'twould be a sin to
cut another sentence in two,
Send it in, and we'll begin to—boil it down.

One last word. If you are aware that a new name is going to be published, be very careful not to use that name yourself in anything that might be published sooner. You run the risk of creating a *nomen nudum*, and infringing on the rights of the scientist who has done the work. There have been cases of someone reporting on a fish soon to be named, and combining the use of the proposed name with just enough of a description to avoid categorizing the name as a *nomen nudum*. In this case, the aquarist becomes the legal author of a valid name, and the person who did all the work is left out in the cold. This use of a name before it has been properly published in a scientific journal is the very worst of bad manners. Often the scientist is as much to blame for using the name in a personal letter to an aquarist unacquainted with the rules, both written and unwritten.

A complete scientific name should be written in the following way:

Example: Cichlasoma ornatum Regan, 1905.

The end part of this name means that the name was first used by Regan in an article published during the year 1905. Many ichthyologists have a tendency to omit the year of the description, and this ought not be done; the year should be given. If the name and year are enclosed in parentheses, it means that this species was originally described within a genus different from the genus in which it is now contained. Any species name referring to the same animal, but published after the earliest name, is a junior synonym and becomes invalid. (There are rare exceptions, but the Commission must rule on any exceptions specifically.) If you see a colon (:) or the word *sensu* occurring between the specific epithet (e.g., *ornatum*) and the man's name, this means that this man was not the one who originally described the species; rather, this man referred to a particular fish with this particular name, and he may have been right or wrong in his application of the name to that fish. Thus, the colon or *sensu* means only that he used the name, and not that he coined it.

Cunningtonia longiventralis, from Lake Tanganyika. This is the only species in the genus. Photo by Paul V. Loiselle.

Bibliography

Angier, S. 1970. Observations on *Aequidens geayi*. Adv. Aquar. Atlanta Newsl. No. 14:7.

Apfelbach, R. 1970. Correlated aggressive and brooding behavior patterns in Tilapia. Z. vergl. Physiol. *68*: 293–300.

—— and D. Leong. 1970. Zum Kampfverhalten in der Gattung *Tilapia*. Z. f. Tierpsychol. *27*: 98–107.

Aronson, L. R. 1948. Problems in the behavior and physiology of a species of African mouthbreeding fish. Trans. N.Y. Acad. Sci., ser. 2, *11*: 33–42.

Astorqui, I. S. J. 1971. Peces de la cuenca do los grandes lagos de Nicaragua. Rev. Biol. Trop. *19*: 7–57.

Badawi, H. K. and M. M. Said. 1971. A comparative study of the blood of four *Tilapia* species. Mar. Biol. *8*: 202–204.

Baerends, G. P. and J. M. Baerends. 1950. An introduction to the study of the ethology of cichlid fishes. Behaviour, suppl. *1*: 1–242.

Baker, B. I. 1964. Pituitary-thyroid relationship during development in the teleost *Herichthys cyanoguttatus*: a histophysiologic study. Gen. Comp. Endocrinol. *4*: 164–175.

Barlow, G. W. 1968. Effect of size of mate on courtship in a cichlid fish, *Etroplus maculatus*. Commun. Behav. Biol., A, *2*: 149–160.

—— 1970. A test of appeasement and arousal hypotheses of courtship behavior in a cichlid fish, *Etroplus maculatus*. Z. Tierpsychol. *27*: 779–806.

—— and R. F. Green. 1969. Effect of relative size of mate on color pattern in a mouthbreeding cichlid fish, *Tilapia melanotheron*. Commun. Behav. Biol., A, *4*: 71–78.

—— —— 1970. The problems of appeasement and of sexual roles in the courtship behavior of the blackchin mouthbreeder, *Tilapia melanotheron*. Behaviour *36*: 84–115.

Bauer, J. 1968. Vergleichende Untersuchungen zum Kontaktverhalten verschiedener Arten der Gattung *Tilapia* und ihre Bastarde. Z. Tierpsychol. *25*: 22–70.

Beauchamp, R. S. A. 1964. The Rift Valley Lakes of Africa. Verh. Intern. Verein. Limnol. *15*: 91–99.

Bergmann, H. H. 1971. Untersuchungen zur Verhaltensentwicklung beim Segelflosser (*Pterophyllum scalare* Cu. v & Val., Cichlidae). Z. Tierpsychol. *29*: 343–388.

Blum, V. 1968a. Die Auslosung des Laichreflexes durch Reserpin bei dem sudamerikanischen Buntbarsch *Pterophyllum scalare*. Z. vergl. Physiol. *60*: 79–81.

—— 1968b. Experimente zum Steuerungsmechanismus hormoninduzierter Brutpflegereaktionen beim Buntbarsch *Pterophyllum scalare*. Z. vergl. Physiol. *61*: 21–33.

—— and K. Fiedler. 1965. Hormonal control of reproductive behavior in some cichlid fish. Gen. Comp. Endocrinol. *5*: 186–196.

Boulenger, G. A. 1898. Report on the collection of fishes made by Mr. J. E. S. Moore in Lake Tanganyika during his expedition, 1895–1896. Trans. Zool. Soc. Lond. 15, *1*: 1–30.

—— 1915. Catalogue of the fresh-water fishes of Africa in the British Museum (Natural History), vols. 3, 4. Reprinted, 1964, Wheldon and Wesley, Codicote, Herts., England.

Brick, M. J. 1970. Observations on two species of Lake Tanganyika cichlids. Adv. Aquar. Atlanta Newsl. No. 11: 2.

Brinley, F. J. and L. Eulberg. 1953. Embryological head glands of the cichlid fish *Aequidens portalegrensis*. Copeia *1953*: 24–26.

Britski, H. A. and J. A. Luengo. 1968. Sobre *Crenicichla jupiaensis* sp. n., especie aberrante, do Rio Parana. Papeis Avulsos Zool. *21*: 169–182.

Burchard, J., Jr. and W. Wickler. 1965. Eine neue Form des cichliden *Hemichromis fasciatus* Peters. Z. Zool. Syst. Evolutionsforsch. *3*: 227–283.

Bussing, W. A. 1967. New species and new records of Costa Rican fresh-water fishes with a tentative list of species. Rev. Biol. Trop. *14*: 205–249.

Caldwell, M. W. 1971. The new falsemouth cichlid. Adv. Aquar. Mag. No. 24: 2.

Campbell, C. 1970. *Julidochromis ornatus*. Buntb. Bull. No. 24: 26–27.

Campbell, V. 1970. *Nanochromis dimidiatus*. Adv. Aquar. Atlanta Newsl. No. 9: 8.

Chervinski, J. 1968a. The cichlids of Ein-Feshkha Springs. I. *Tilapia aurea exul* (Steinitz). Hydrobiologia *32*: 150–156.

—— 1968b. The cichlids of Ein-Feshkha Springs. II. *Tilapia zillii* (Gervais). Op. cit. *32*: 157–160.

Coe, M. J. 1966. The biology of *Tilapia grahami* Boulenger in Lake Magadi, Kenya. Acta Trop. *23*: 146–177.

Cole, J. E. and J. A. Ward. 1969. The communicative function of pelvic fin-flickering in *Etroplus maculatus*. Behaviour *35*: 179–199.

—— —— 1970. An analysis of parental recognition by the young of the cichlid fish, *Etroplus maculatus* (Bloch). Z. Tierpsychol. *27*: 156–176.

Culpepper, B. 1971. *Hemichromis fasciatus* Type B. Adv. Aquar. Mag. No. 22: 7.

Dadzie, S. 1968. The structure of the chorion of the egg of the mouth-brooding cichlid fish *Tilapia mossambica*. J. Zool. London. *154*: 161–163.

Daget, J. 1962. Les poissons du Fouta Dialon et de la basse Guinee. Mem. I.F.A.N., 210 pp., 61 figs., 13 pls.

—— and P. DeRham. 1970. Sur quelques poissons du Sud de la Cote d'Ivoire. Rev. Suisse Zool. *77*: 801–806.

David, L. and M. Poll. 1937. Contribution a la faune ichthyologique du Congu Belge: collections du Dr. H. Schouteden (1924–1926) et d'autres recolteurs. Ann. Mus. Congo Belg., Zool., ser. 1, *3*: 189–294, pl. XII.

Eckstein, B. and Y. Katz. 1971. Steroidogenesis in post- and pre-spawned ovaries of a cichlid fish, *Tilapia aurea*. Comp. Biochem. Physiol. *38A*: 329–338.

—— and M. Spira. 1966. Sterilization of the cichlid fish *Tilapia aurea*. Israel J. Zool. *15*: 31.

Eibl-Eibesfeldt, I. and S. Kramer. 1958. Ethology, the comparative study of animal behavior. Quart. Rev. Biol. *33*: 181–211.

Eigenmann, C. 1924. Fishes of northwestern South America. Mem. Carnegie Mus. *9*: 1–277.

—— and W. R. Allen. 1942. Fishes of Western South America, Waverly Press, 494 pp., map.

—— and R. S. Eigenmann. 1891. A catalogue of the freshwater fishes of South America. Proc. U.S.N.M. *14*: 1–81.

Evermann, B. W. and E. L. Goldsborough. 1902. A report on fishes collected in Mexico and Central America, with notes and descriptions of five new species. Bull. U.S. Fish Comm. *21*: 137–159.

Fagade, S. O. 1971. The food and feeding habits of *Tilapia* species in the Lagos Lagoon. J. Fish Biol. *3*: 151–156.

Fernandez-Yepez, A. 1950. Notas sobre la fauna ictiologica de Venezuela. Mem. Soc. Cien. Nat. LaSalle (Caracas) *10*: 111–118.

Fishelson, V. L. 1966. Untersuchungen zur vergleichenden Entwicklungsgeschichte der Gattung *Tilapia*. Zool. Jb. Anat. *83*: 571–656.

—— 1967. Cichlidae of the genus *Tilapia* in Israel. Bamidgeh *18*: 67–80.

Fowler, H. W. 1937. A collection of Haitian fishes obtained by Mr. Stanley Woodward. Proc. Acad. Nat. Sci. Phila. *89*: 309–315.

—— 1938. A smaller collection of freshwater fishes from eastern Cuba. Op. cit. *90*: 143–147.

—— 1939. A collection of fishes obtained by Mr. William C. Morrow in the Ucayali River basin, Peru. Op. cit. *91*: 219–289.

—— 1940. Zoological results of the second Bolivian expedition, 1936–1937, Part 1, The Fishes. Op. cit. *92*: 43–103.

—— 1944. Freshwater fishes from northwestern Colombia. Op. cit. *96*: 227–248.

—— 1954. Os peixes de agua doce do Brasil. Arq. Zool. Est. Sao Paulo *9*: 1–400.

Fryer, G. 1959. The trophic interrelationships and ecology of some littoral communities of Lake Nyasa with especial reference to the fishes, and a discussion of the evolution of a group of rock-frequenting cichlidae. Proc. Zool. Soc. Lond. *132*: 153–281.

—— 1957. A new species of *Gephyrochromis* from Lake Nyasa, with notes on its ecology and affinities. Rev. Zool. Bot. Afr. *55*: 347–352.

—— 1964. Further studies on the parasitic crustacea of African freshwater fishes. Proc. Zool. Soc. Lond. *143*: 79–102.

—— P. H. Greenwood and E. Trewavas. 1955. Scale-eating habits of African cichlid fishes. Nature *175*: 1089.

—— and T. D. Iles. 1955. Predation pressure and evolution in Lake Nyasa. Nature *176*: 470.

—— —— 1969. Alternative routes to evolutionary success as exhibited by African cichlid fishes of the genus *Tilapia* and the species flocks of the Great Lakes. Evolution *23*: 359–369.

Gallagher, J. E., M. J. Herz, and H. V. S. Peeke. 1972. Habituation of aggression: the effects of visual social stimuli on behavior between adjacently territorial convict cichlids (*Cichlasoma nigrofasciatum*). Behav. Biol. *7*: 359–368.

Gery, J. 1969. The freshwater fishes of South America, *in* Biogeography and Ecology in South America, E. J. Fittkau et al., Eds., Junk N.V.

The Hague, pp. 828–848.
Gianladis, G. and R. Olson. 1970. A study of territoriality and color. Buntb. Bull. No. 21: 14–25.
Gilbert, C. R. and D. P. Kelso. 1971. Fishes of the Tortuguero area, Caribbean Costa Rica. Bull. Fla. State Mus. (Biol. Sci.) *16*: 1–54.
Girdler, R. W., Fairhead, J. D., Searle, R. C. and W. T. C. Sowerbutts. 1969. Evolution of rifting in Africa. Nature *224*: 1178–1182.
Goldstein, R. J. 1967. *Nannacara anomala*. Aquarium *36* (1): 6 ff.
—— 1970a. A brief review of the genus *Apistogramma*. Adv. Aquar. Atlanta Newsl. No. 8: 4–5.
—— 1970b. The identification of the green terror cichlid. Op. cit. No. 13: 6.
—— 1970c. Cichlids, T.F.H., Neptune City, 254 pp.
—— 1971. Diseases of Aquarium Fishes, T.F.H., Neptune City, 126 pp.
—— and G. D. Jordan. 1970. The new green terror. Adv. Aquar. Atlanta Newsl. No. 10: 8.
Gosse, J.-P. 1963. Description de deux cichlides nouveaux de la region Amazonienne. Inst. Roy. Soc. Nat. Belg. Bull. *39*: 1–7.
Gosse, J. P. 1971. Revision du genre *Retroculus* Eigenmann & Bray, 1894, designation d'un neotype de *Retroculus lapidifer* (Castelnau, 1855) et description de deux especies nouvelles. Bull. Inst. r. Sci. nat. Belg. *47* (43): 1–13.
Greenberg, B., Zijlstra, J. J. and G. P. Baerend. 1965. A quantitative description of the behavior changes during the reproductive cycle of the cichlid fish *Aequidens portalegrensis* Hensel. Konink. Nederl. Akad. Wten-Amstr., Proc., ser. C, *68*: 135–149.
Greenwald, J. 1971. The mystery fish. Cichlid Power (San Diego) *1* (6): 5–6.
Greenwood, P. H. 1956. The monotypic genera of cichlid fishes in Lake Victoria. Bull. Brit. Mus. (Nat. Hist.) Zool. *3*: 295–333.
—— 1959. A revision of the Lake Victoria *Haplochromis* species, Part III. Op. cit. *5*: 179–218.
—— 1960. A revision . . ., Part IV. Op. cit. *6*: 227–281.
—— 1962. A revision . . ., Part V. Op. cit. *9*: 139–214.
—— 1964. Explosive speciation in African lakes. Proc. Roy. Inst. G.B. *40* (III, 184): 256–269.
—— 1965. Two new species of *Haplochromis* from Lake Victoria. Ann. Mag. Nat. Hist. Ser. 13, *8*: 303–318, p. XI.
—— 1967. A revision . . ., Part VI. Bull. Brit. Mus. (Nat. Hist.) Zool. *15*: 29–119.
—— and J. M. Gee. 1969. A revision . . ., Part VII. Op. cit. *18*: 1–65.
—— Rosen, D. E., Weitzman, S. H. and G. S. Myers. 1966. Phyletic studies of teleostean fishes, with a provisional classification of living forms. Bull. Amer. Mus. Nat. Hist. *131*: 339–456.
Greenwood, P. H. 1971. On the cichlid fish *Halochromis wingatii* (Blgr.), and a new species from the Nile and Lake Albert. Rev. Zool. Bot. Afr. *84*: 344–365.
Haseman, J. D. 1911. An annotated catalogue of the cichlid fishes collected by the expedition of the Carnegie Museum to central South America, 1907–10. Ann. Carnegie Mus. *7*: 329–373.

Heiligenberg, W. 1965a. A quantitative analysis of digging movements and their relationship to aggressive behavior in cichlids. Anim. Behav. *13*: 163–170.

—— 1965b. Color polymorphism in the males of an African cichlid fish. J. Zool. *146*: 95–97.

—— 1965c. The suppression of behavioral activities by frightening stimuli. Z. vergl. Physiol. *50*: 660–672.

Heiligenberg, W., U. Kramer, and V. Schultz. 1972. The angular orientation of the black eye-bar in *Haplochromis burtoni* and its relevance to aggressivity. Z. vergl. Physiol. *76*: 168–176.

Hubbs, C. L. 1936. Fishes of the Yucatan Peninsula. Carnegie Inst. Wash. Publ. No. 457: 157–287, pls. 1–15.

—— 1953. Geographic and systematic status of the fishes described by Kner and Steindachner in 1863 and 1865 from fresh waters in Panama and Ecuador. Copeia *1953*: 141–148.

Huizinga, H. W. 1972. Pathobiology of *Artystone trysibia* Schioedte (Isopoda: Cymothoidae), an endoparasitic isopod of South American fresh water fishes. J. Wildlife Dis. *8*: 225–232.

Hyder, M. 1969. Gonadal development and reproductive activity of the cichlid fish, *Tilapia leucosticta* (Trewavas) in an equatorial lake. Nature *224*: 1112.

—— 1970a. Gonadal and reproductive patterns in *Tilapia leucosticta* in an equatorial lake, Lake Naivasha (Kenya). J. Zool. Lond. *162*: 179–195.

—— 1970b. Histological studies on the testes of pond specimens of *Tilapia nigra* (Gunther) and their implications of the pituitary-testis relationship. Gen. Comp. Endocrin. *14*: 198–211.

Iles, T. D. and M. J. Holden. 1969. Bi-parental mouth brooding in *Tilapia galilaea*. J. Zool. Lond. *158*: 327–333.

Iles, T. D. 1971. Ecological aspects of growth in African cichlid fishes. J. Cons. int. Explor. Mer *33*: 363–385.

Innes, W. T. 1951. Exotic Aquarium Fishes, 12 Ed., Innes Pub. Co., Phila., 521 pp.

Jones, A. J. 1972. The early development of substrate-brooding cichlids with a discussion of a new system of staging. J. Morphol. *136*: 255–272.

Jordan, D. S. and B. W. Evermann. 1898. The fishes of North and Middle America. Bull. U.S.N.M. No. *47*, Part III, pp. 1512–1543.

—— and J. O. Snyder. 1901. Notes on a collection of fishes from the rivers of Mexico, with descriptions of twenty new species. Bull. U.S. Fish Comm. *19*: 115–147.

Jubb, R. A. 1967. Freshwater Fishes of Southern Africa, A. A. Balkema, Capetown, 248 pp.

Kiener, A. and M. Mauge. 1966. Contributions a l'etude systematique et ecologique des poissons cichlidae endemiques de Madagascar. Mem. Mus. Nat. Hist. Nat., Nouv. ser. *40*: 4–99, 4 pls.

Kirk, R. G. 1972. A review of recent developments in *Tilapia* culture, with special reference to fish farming in the heated effluents of power stations. Aquaculture *1*: 45–60.

Klee, A. J. 1971. A note on the name of *Apistogramma ramirezi*. Aquarium *4* (5): 47–48.

Kleinhout, J. 1965. On experiments with Yohimbine on the jewel fish, *Hemichromis bimaculatus*. Zool. Anz. *174*: 399–400.

Kohn, A. and I. Paperna. 1964. Monogenetic trematodes from aquarium fishes. Rev. Brasil. Biol. *24*: 145–149.

Kuenzer, P. 1962a. Wie erkennen Cichliden-Junge ihre Eltern? I. D.A.T.Z. *15* (11): 332–334.

—— 1962b. Wie erkenne . . .? II. D.A.T.Z. *15* (12): 362–365.

—— 1962c. Die Auslosung der Nachfolgereaktion durch Bewegungsreize bei Jungfischen von *Nannacara anomala* Regan. Naturwissenschaften *49*: 525–526.

—— 1964. Weitere Versuche zur Auslosung der Nachfolgereaktion bei Jungfische von *Nannacara anomala*. Naturwissenschaften *51*: 419–420.

—— 1965. Zur optischen Auslosung von Brutpflegehandlungen bei *Nannacara anomala* weibchenen. Naturwissenschaften *52*: 19–20.

Kühme, W. 1964a. Eine chemisch ausgeloste Brutpflegereaktion bei Cichliden. Naturwissenschaften *51*: 20–21.

—— 1964b. Eine chemisch ausgeloste Schwarmreaktion bei jungen Cichliden. Naturwissenschaften *51*: 120–121.

Lachner, E. A., Robins, C. R., and W. R. Courtenay, Jr. 1970. Exotic fishes and other aquatic organisms introduced into North America. Smithsonian Contr. Zool. *59*: 1–29.

LaCorte, R. 1970. Spawning Lake Tanganyika's *Julidochromis ornatus*. Trop. Fish World *2* (1): 4 ff.

Lagler, K. F., Bardach, J. E., and R. R. Miller. 1962. Ichthyology, Wiley and Sons, N.Y., 545 pp.

Langescheid, C. 1968. Vergleichende Untersuchungen über die angeborone Grossenunterscheidung bei *Tilapia nilotica* und *Hemihaplochromis multicolor*. Experientia *24*. 963–964.

Lanzing, W. J. R. 1965. Observations on malachite green in relation to its application to fish diseases. Hydrobiologia *25*: 426–440.

—— 1971. Effects of some anaesthetics on laboratory-reared *Tilapia mossambica*. Copeia *1971*: 182–184.

Leong, C. Y. 1969. The quantitative effect of releasers on the attack readiness of the fish *Haplochromis burtoni*. Z. vergl. Physiol. *65*: 29–50.

Lincoln, R. J. 1972. A new species of *Lironeca* (Isopoda: Cymothoidae) parasitic on cichlid fishes in Lake Tanganyika. Bull. Brit. Mus. Nat. Hist. (Zool.) *21*: 329–338.

Lindquist, B. 1971. *Lamprologus* species. Buntb. Bull. No. 26: 9–11, 15.

Liu, D. H. W., Krueger, H. and W. Chih. 1970. Catabolic pathways for glucose in the cichlid fish, *Cichlasoma bimaculatum*. Comp. Biochem. Physiol. *36*: 173–181.

Loiselle, P. V. 1967. The cupido cichlid. Aquar. Illust. *2* (3): 16–23.

—— 1969. Monographie systematique et notes biologiques sur les poissons de la lagune de Lomé. Bull. Benin (Lomé, Togo), 37 pp.

—— 1970. The current status of the genus *Pelmatochromis* Hubrecht sensu lato. Buntb. Bull. No. 20: 17–21.

—— 1971a. An unusual African mouthbrooder, *Chromidotilapia guentheri*. Afr. Aquar. *4* (4): 4–8.

—— 1971b. Hybridization in cichlids. Buntb. Bull. No. 27: 9–18.

Loiselle, P. V. and R. L. Welcomme. 1972. Description of a new genus of cichlid fish from West Africa. Rev. Zool. Bot. Afr. *85*: 37–58.

Longfellow, J. 1970. Spawning the pike cichlid. Buntb. Bull. No. 22: 7–8.
Lopez-Sanchez, M. I. 1968. Clave para los peces de la aguas continentales de Costa Rica. Univ. C. R., Dept. Biol., Costa Rica, 31 pp.
Lowe-McConnell, R. H. 1959. Breeding behavior patterns and ecological differences between *Tilapia* species and their significance for evolution within the genus *Tilapia*. Proc. Zool. Soc. Lond. *132*: 1–30.
—— 1969. The cichlid fishes of Guyana, South America, with notes on their ecology and breeding behaviour. Zool. J. Linn. Soc. *48*: 255–302.
Mark, R. F. and A. Maxwell. 1969. Circle size discrimination and transposition behaviour in cichlid fish. Anim. Behav. *17*: 155–158.
Marlier, G. and N. Leleup. 1954. A curious ecological "niche" among the fishes of Lake Tanganyika. Nature *174*: 936.
Mattheij, J. A. M. and H. W. J. Stroband. 1971. The effects of osmotic experiments and prolactin on the mucous cells in the skin and the ionocytes in the gills of the teleost *Cichlasoma biocellatum*. Z. Zellforsch. *121*: 93–101.
Mattheij, J. A. M., F. J. Kingma, and H. W. J. Stroband. 1971. The identification of the thyrotropic cells in the adenohypophysis of the cichlid fish *Cichlasoma biocellatum* and the role of these cells and of the thyroid in osmoregulation. Z. Zellforsch. *121*: 82–92.
Meinken, H. 1961. *Apistogramma borelli* (Regan). D.A.T.Z. *14* (6): 166–169.
—— 1962a. Eine notwendige Richtigstellung. (*A. borelli*). Op. cit. *15* (3): 70–72.
—— 1962b. Eine neue *Apistogramma*-Art aus dem mittleren Amazonas-Gebeit, zugleich mit dem Versuch einer Übersicht uber die Gattung. Senck. Biol. *43*: 137–143.
—— 1964. *Apistogramma kleei* spec. nov., der Querbinden-Zwergbarsch. D.A.T.Z. *17* (10): 293–297.
—— 1965a. Uber eine neue Gattung und Art der Familie Cichlidae aus Peru. Senck. Biol. *46*: 47–53.
—— 1965b. Eine neue *Apistogramma*-Art aus Venezuela. Senck. Biol. *46*: 257–263.
—— 1969. *Apistogramma gibbiceps* n. sp. aus Brasilien. Senck. Biol. *50*: 91–96.
—— 1970. *Apistogramma gibbiceps*, a new species from Brazil. Buntb. Bull. No. 24: 7–10.
Meinken, H. 1971. *Apistogramma geisleri* n. sp. und *Apistogramma borellii* (Regan) aus dem Amazonas-Becken. Senckenberg. Biol. *52*: 35–40.
Miller, R. R. 1966. Geographical distribution of Central American freshwater fishes. Copeia *1966*: 773–802.
—— and B. C. Nelson. 1961. Variation, life colors, and ecology of *Cichlasoma callolepis*, a cichlid fish from southern Mexico, with a discussion of the *Thorichthys* species group. Occ. Pap. Mus. Zool., Univ. Mich., No. 622, 9 pp.
Monfort-Braham, N. and J. Voss. 1969. Contribution a l'ethologie des poissons cichlides: *Tilapia tholloni* (Sauvage, 1884). Ann. Soc. Roy. Zool. Belg. *99*: 59–68.
Montgomery, B. 1971. Spawning a new *Geophagus*. Buntb. Bull. No. 27: 24–25.

Morris, R. W. 1962. Body size and temperature sensitivity in the cichlid fish, Aequidens portalegrensis (Hensel). Amer. Natur. *96*: 35–50.
Myers, G. S. 1936. Report on the fishes collected by H. C. Raven in Lake Tanganyika in 1920. Proc. U.S.N.M. *84*: 1–13.
—— 1960. Fish evolution in Lake Nyasa. Evolution *14*: 394–396.
—— 1964. A brief history of ichthyology in America to the year 1850. Copeia *1964*: 33–60.
—— 1966. Derivation of the freshwater fish fauna of Central America. Copeia *1966*: 766–773.
Myrberg, A. A., Jr. 1965. A descriptive analysis of the behavior of the African cichlid fish, *Pelmatochromis guentheri* (Sauvage), Anim. Behav. *13*: 312–329.
—— 1966. Parental recognition of young in cichlid fishes. Anim. Behav. *14*: 565–571.
—— Kramer, E. and P. Heinecke. 1965. Sound production by cichlid fishes. Science *149*: 555–558.
Nussbaum, M. and J. Chervinsky. 1968. Artificial incubation of *Tilapia nilotica*. Bamidgeh *20*: 120–124.
Olson, R. D. 1970. *Cichlasoma dowi*. Adv. Aquar. Atlanta Newsl. No. 16: 8.
—— and G. Gianladis. 1970a. Parental care and behavior in cichlids. Buntb. Bull. No. 22: 18–19.
—— —— 1970b. The Friedrichsthal's cichlid. Op. cit. No. 23: 13–15.
Ovchynnyk, M. M. 1968. Annotated list of the freshwater fish of Ecuador. Zool. Anz. *181*: 237–268.
Ovchynnyk, M. M. 1971. Unrecorded and new species of fishes from fresh waters of Ecuador. Zool. Anz. *187*: 82–122.
Paperna, I. 1960. Studies on monogenetic trematodes in Israel. 2. Monogenetic trematodes of cichlids. Bamidgeh *12*: 20–33.
—— 1963. *Enterogyrus cichlidarum* n. gen. n. sp., a monogenetic trematode parasitic in the intestine of a fish. Bull. Res. Counc. Israel, B, Zool., *11*: 183–187.
—— 1965. Monogenetic trematodes collected from freshwater fish in southern Ghana. Bamidgeh *17*: 107-111.
—— 1968a. Monogenetic trematodes collected from freshwater fish in Ghana. Second report. Op. cit. *20*: 88–100.
—— 1968b. *Onchobdella* n. gen. New genus of monogenetic trematodes (Dactylogyridae, Bychowsky 1933) from cichlid fish from West Africa. Proc. Helm. Soc. Wash. *35*: 200–206.
Parvatheswararao, V. 1967. Some mechanisms underlying thermal acclimation in a freshwater fish, *Etroplus maculatus*. Comp. Biochem. Physiol. *21*: 619–626.
Peeke, H. V. S., M. J. Herz, and J. E. Gallagher. 1971. Changes in aggressive interaction in adjacently territorial convict cichlids *(Cichlasoma nigrofasciatum)*: a study of habituation. Behaviour *40*: 43–54.
Peters, H. M. 1965a. Angeborenes Verhalten bei Buntbarschen. I. Wege der Analyse. Umschau *21*: 665–670.
—— 1965b. Angeborenes . . . II. Das Problem der erblichen Grundlage des Kontaktverhaltens. Op. cit. *22*: 711–718.
Pienaar, U. de V. 1968. The freshwater fishes of the Kruger National

Park. Publ. Nat. Parks Bd. Trustees Rep. South Africa, 82 pp., 46 figs.
Poll, M. 1932. Contribution a la faune des cichlidae du Lac Kivu (Congo Belge). Description d'une espece nouvelle d'*Haplochromis* et d'une espece nouvelle de *Tilapia*. Rev. Zool. Bot. Afr. *23*: 29–35.
—— 1933. L'evolution des poissons africains de la famille des cichlidae. Rev. Zool. Bot. Afr. *24*: 203–209.
—— 1942. Cichlidae nouveaux du Lac Tanganika appartenant aux collections du Musee du Congo. Rev. Zool. Bot. Afr. *36*: 343–360.
—— 1943. Descriptions de poissons nouveaux du Lac Tanganika, appartenant aux familles des Clariidae et Cichlidae. Rev. Zool. Bot. Afr. *37*: 305–318.
—— 1944. Descriptions de poissons nouveaux recueillis dans la region l'Albertville (Congo Belge) par le Dr. G. Pojer. Bull. Mus. Roy. Hist. Nat. Belg. *20*: 1–12.
—— 1948a. L'etat actuel de nos connaissances sur la faune ichthyologique du Lac Tanganika. Bull. Agric. Congo Belg. *39*: 119–126.
—— 1948b. Rapport preliminaire sur la peche au Lac Tanganika. Op. cit. *39*: 127–130.
—— 1948c. Descriptions de cichlidae nouveaux recueillis par la mission hydrobiologique belge au Lac Tanganika (1946–1947). Konink. Nat. Mus. Belg. *24* (26): 1–31.
—— 1948d. Descriptions de cichlidae nouveaux recueillis par le Dr. J. Schwetz dans la riviere Fwa (Congo Belge). Rev. Zool. Bot. Afr. *41*: 91–104.
—— 1949. Deuxieme serie de cichlidae nouveaux recueillis par la mission . . . (1946–1947). Konink. Nat. Mus. Belg. *25*: 1–55.
—— 1950a. Description de deux cichlidae petricoles du Lac Tanganika. Rev. Zool. Bot. Afr. *43*: 292–302.
—— 1950b. Histoire du peuplement et origine des especes de la faune ichthyologique du Lac Tanganika. Ann. Soc. Roy. Zool. Belg. *81*: 111–140, pls. 1–3.
—— 1951a. Troisieme serie de cichlidae nouveaux recueillis par la mission . . . (1946–1947). Konink. Belg. Inst. Nat. *27* (29): 1–11.
—— 1951b. Troisieme . . . (1946–1947). Suite 1. Op. cit. *27* (30): 1–12.
—— 1951c. Troisieme . . . (1946–1947). Suite 2. Op. cit. *27* (31): 1–8.
—— 1952. Quatrieme serie . . . (1946–1947). Op. cit. *28* (49): 1–20.
—— 1956a. Ecologie des poissons du Lac Tanganika. Proc. XIV Int. Cong. Zool., Copenhagen, 1953: 465–468.
—— 1956b. Poissons cichlidae. Explor. Hydrobiol. Lac Tanganika 3, *5B*, Inst. Roy. Soc. Sci. Nat. Belg., Tervuren, Belgium.
—— 1967. Contribution a la faune ichthyologique de l'Angola. Mus. do Dundo (Lisbon), Publ. Cult. No. 75, 381 pp.
—— and D. F. E. Thys van den Audenaerde. 1960. Existence dans la foret equatoriale congolaise d'une nouvelle sous-espece de *Tilapia* caraterisee par une gibbosite frontale, *Tilapia tholloni congica* subsp. nov. Rev. Zool. Bot. Afr. *62*: 329–339.
—— —— 1965. Deux cichlidae nouveaux du Sud du Bassin du Congo. Rev. Zool. Bot. Afr. *72*: 322–333.
—— —— 1967. Description de *Pelmatochromis schoutedeni* sp. n. du Congo oriental. Rev. Zool. Bot. Afr. *75*: 383–391.
Price, C. E. 1966. *Urocleidus cavanaughi*, a new monogenetic trematode

from the gills of the keyhole cichlid, *Aequidens maroni* (Steindachner). Bull. Ga. Acad. Sci. *24*: 117–120.

—— 1967a. The freshwater monogenetic trematodes of South America. Rev. di Parassit. *28*: 87–95.

—— 1967b. The freshwater monogenetic trematodes of Africa. Rev. Zool. Bot. Afr. *76*: 375–391.

—— and E. A. Schlueter. 1968. Two new monogenetic trematodes from South America. J. Tenn. Acad. Sci. for 1968: 23–25.

Privat, F. 1970. Contribution a l'etude du mode de nutrition du *Tilapia rendalli*. Rev. Suisse Zool. 77: 61–79.

Quertermus, C. J., Jr. and J. A. Ward. 1969. Development and significance of two motor patterns used in contacting parents by young orange chromides (*Etroplus maculatus*). Anim. Behav. *17*: 624–635.

Regan, C. T. 1905a. A revision of the South American cichlid genera *Crenacara, Batrachops* and *Crenicichla*. Proc. Zool Soc. Lond. *1*: 152–168.

—— 1905b. A revision of the fishes of the South-American cichlid genera *Acara, Nannacara, Acaropsis* and *Astronotus*. Ann. Mag. Nat. Hist., ser. 7, *15*: 329–347.

—— 1905c. A revision of the American cichlid genus *Cichlasoma* and of the allied genera. Ann. Mag. Nat. Hist., ser. 7, *16*: 60–77, 225–243, 316–340.

—— 1906. A revision of the South American cichlid genera *Retroculus, Geophagus, Heterogramma* and *Biotoecus*. Ann. Mag. Nat. Hist., ser. 7, *17*: 49–66.

—— 1908. Pisces, *in* Biologia Centrali-Americana, pp. 1–203, pls. 1–26, maps 1, 2.

—— 1921a. The cichlid fishes of Lakes Albert Edward and Kivu. Ann. Mag. Nat. Hist., ser. 9, *8*: 632–639.

—— 1921b. The cichlid fishes of Lake Nyassa. Proc. Zool. Soc. Lond. *91*: 675–727.

—— 1922. The cichlid fishes of Lake Victoria. Proc. Zool. Soc. Lond. *92*: 157–191.

Reid, M. J. and J. W. Atz. 1958. Oral incubation in the cichlid fish *Geophagus jurupari* Heckel. Zoologica *43* (3): 77–88.

Richter, H. J. 1969. *Nannochromis nudiceps*. Trop. Fish Hobbyist *17* (5): 36 ff.

Riedel, D. 1972. Die Genesis der nicaraguensischen Grabenseen (Teil I) und des mesoamerikanischen Isthmus (Teil II) aus der Sicht des Fischereibiologen (the origin of the lakes in the Nicaraguan fault and of the Middle American isthmus in the light of studies of the fish fauna). Arch. Hydrobiol. *70*: 82–107.

Rivas, L. R. 1962. *Cichlasoma pasionis*, a new species of cichlid fish of the *Thorichthys* group, from the Rio de la Pasion, Guatemala. Quart. J. Fla. Acad. Sci. *25*: 147–156.

Robinson, A. H. and P. K. Robinson. 1971. Seasonal distribution of zoo plankton in the northern basin of Lake Chad. J. Zool. Lond. *163*: 25–61.

Roman, B. 1965. Les poissons des Hant-Bassins de la Volta. Mus. Roy. Afr. Centr., Ann. Sci. Zool., ser. 8, No. 150: 1–191.

Ruwet, J. C. 1968. Familial behavior of *Tilapia* and its implications.

Nature *217*: 977.
Schleser, D. 1971. The Texas cichlid. Adv. Aquar. Mag. No. 20: 1.
Schultz, L. P. 1944. A new species of cichlid fish of the genus *Petenia* from Colombia. J. Wash. Acad. Sci. *34*: 410–412.
—— 1949. A further contribution to the ichthyology of Venezuela. Proc. U.S.N.M. *99*: 1–211, pls. 1–3.
—— 1967. Review of South American freshwater angelfishes—genus *Pterophyllum*. Proc. U.S.N.M. *120*: 1–10.
Sividas, P. 1965. Absorption of fat in the alimentary canal of *Tilapia mossambica*. J. Cell. Comp. Physiol. *65*: 249–253.
Sprenger, K. 1970. Spawning and parental care of two *Geophagus* species. Buntb. Bull. No. 24: 15–17.
—— 1971. The red hump *Geophagus*. Buntb. Bull. No. 26: 24–25.
Sterba, G. 1959. Freshwater fishes of the World, Viking Press, N.Y., 878 pp.
Stevens, E. D. and F. E. J. Fry. 1970. The rate of thermal exchange in a teleost, *Tilapia mossambica*. Can. J. Zool. *48*: 221–226.
Svensson, G. S. O. 1933. Fresh water fishes from the Gambia River (British West Africa). Results of the Swedish expedition 1931. Kungl. Svenska Vetensk. Handl., ser. 3, *12*: 2–102, pls. 1–8.
Temple, P. H. 1969. Some biological implications of a revised geological history for Lake Victoria. Biol. J. Linn. Soc. *1*: 363–371.
Thomerson, J. E. and D. W. Greenfield. 1972. Preliminary key to the freshwater fishes of Belize (British Honduras), mimeographed.
Thys van den Audenaerde, D. F. E. 1968a. A preliminary contribution to a systematic revision of the genus *Pelmatochromis* Hubrecht sensu lato. Rev. Zool. Bot. Afr. 77: 351–391.
—— 1968b. Les *Tilapia* du Sud Cameroun et du Gabon. Etude systematique. Ann. Mus. Roy. Afr. Centr., Ser. 8, Sci. Zool. *153*: 1–98.
—— 1968c. An annotated bibliography of *Tilapia*. Documentation Zoologique No. 14, Mus. Roy. Afr. Centr., Tervuren (Belgium), I–XI, 1–406.
Thys v.d. Audenaerde, D. F. E. and P. V. Loiselle. 1971. Description of two new small African cichlids. Rev. Zool. Bot. Afr. *83* (3, 4): 193–206.
Trewavas, E. 1935. A synopsis of the cichlid fishes of Lake Nyasa. Ann. Mag. Nat. Hist. (10) *16*: 65–118.
—— 1946. The types of cichlid fishes described by Borodin in 1931 and 1936, and of two species described by Boulenger in 1901. Proc. Zool. Soc. Lond. *116*: 240–246.
Trewavas, E. 1964. A revision of the genus *Serranochromis* Regan (Pisces, Cichlidae). Ann. Mus. Roy. Afr. Centr. Sci. Zool., no. 125: 1–58.
—— 1966. *Tilapia aurea* (Steindachner) and the status of *Tilapia nilotica exul, T. monodi* and *T. lemassoni*. Israel J. Zool. *14*: 258–276.
—— and M. Poll. 1952. Three new species and two new subspecies of the genus *Lamprologus*, cichlid fishes of Lake Tanganika. Konink. Belg. Inst. Nat. *28* (50): 1–16.
Vilda, D. 1970. Raise discus. Buntb. Bull. No. 25: 13–15.
Villa, J. 1971. Presence of the cichlid fish *Cichlasoma managuense* Günther in Lake Xiloa, Nicaragua. Copeia *1971*: 186.

Wandeler, A. I. 1967. Die Wirbeltiere von Nefta. Beitrag zur Okolgie einer Oase. Jb. Naturh. Mus. Bern 1963–1965, *1967*: 229–292.
Ward, J. A. and G. W. Barlow. 1967. The maturation and regulation of glancing off the parents by young orange chromides (*Etroplus maculatus*). Behaviour *29*: 1–56.
Weber, P. G. 1970. Visual aspects of egg care behaviour in *Cichlasoma nigrofasciatum* (Günther). Anim. Behav. *18*: 688–699.
Weissenberg, R. 1965a. Fifty years of research on the Lymphocystis virus diseases of fishes (1914–1964). Ann. N.Y. Acad. Sci. *126*: 362–374 Acad. Sci. *126*: 396–413.
Welcomme, R. L. 1969. The biology and ecology of the fishes of a small tropical stream. J. Zool. Lond. *158*: 485–529.
Whitehead, R. A. 1966. The life history and breeding habits of the West African cichlid fish *Tilapia mariae* and the status of *T. meeki*. Proc. Zool. Soc. Lond. *139*: 535–543.
Whitfield, J. L. 1970. *Aequidens hercules*. Adv. Aquar. Mag. No. 19: 4–5.
Wickler, W. 1959. The breeding habits of *Teleogramma brichardi*. Trop. Fish Hobbyist, Nov., pp. 16–21.
—— 1965. Neue Varianten des Fortpflanzungsverhaltens afrikanischer Cichliden. Naturwissenschaften *52*: 219.
—— 1966a. Naturliche Ubersexualisierung des Soziallebens beim Brabantbuntbarsch. Umschau Wiss. Tech. *66*: 571–572.
—— 1966b. Sexualdimorphismus, Paarbildung und Versteckbrüten bei Cichliden. Zool. Jhb. Syst. *93*: 127–138.
—— 1966c. Mimicry in tropical fishes. Phil. Trans. Roy. Soc. Lond., B, *251*: 473–474.
—— 1969. Zur Soziologie des Brabantbuntbarsches, *Tropheus moorei*. Z. Tierpsychol. *26*: 967–987.
Wolf, K. 1964. Lymphocystis disease of fish (revised). Fishery leaflet 565, U.S.D.I.: 1–4.
—— Gravell, M. and R. G. Malsberger. 1966. Lymphocystis virus: isolation and propagation in centrarchid fish cell lines. Science *151*: 1004–1005.
Zukal, R. 1971a. Care and breeding of *Pelmatochromis annectens* Boulenger. Afr. Aquar. *4* (5): 11–13.
—— 1971b. Spawning an interesting and colourful African mouthbrooder: *Haplochromis burtoni* (Günther). Afr. Aquar. *4* (8): 7–10.

INDEX

Page numbers in bold type indicate an illustration.

A

B